THE LIBRARY
GUILDFORD COLLEGE
of Further and Higher Education

D1385704

MICRO-ORGANISMS IN ACTION

Peter Freeland

WITHDRAWN

Hodder & Stoughton

LONDON SYDNEY AUCKLAND TORONTO

70971

~~576~~ S79
FRE

CONTENTS

PREFACE

This book is mostly about micro-organisms and their roles in biotechnology. Throughout the book the 5-kingdom system of classification, recommended both by the Institute of Biology and the Association for Science Eduction, has been followed. Micro-organisms belong to three kingdoms: Prokaryotae, Protoctista and Fungi. Their relative simplicity, rapid growth rates and varied roles in nature make them of particular interest to biologists. After years of neglect, possibly on account of their small size, they have moved centre-stage, taken the spotlight, and stimulated much new research.

Along with plants and animals, micro-organisms are currently being used by biotechnologists to manufacture goods or provide services. In biotechnology, biologists and technologists work side by side. The biologists select organisms for commercial enterprises and enhance their usefulness through genetic manipulation. Chemical engineers, along with other technologists, provide the means whereby useful organisms can be cultivated on a large scale, and their products harvested, purified and marketed.

The broad aim of this book is to provide A Level biologists with a modern classification of micro-organisms, and a clear, logical account of the different branches of modern biotechnology, their potential benefits and possible shortcomings. Chapters 1 and 2 deal mainly with the structure and physiology of micro-organisms. Technological advances, such as genetic engineering and the design of fermenters, on which the modern revolution in biotechnology is based, are covered in chapters 3 and 4. The rest of the book illustrates the ways in which biotechnology is being applied in the food industry, in medicine, in agriculture and in environmental control.

MICRO-ORGANISMS: AN INTRODUCTION

Biologists have divided living organisms into major groups called **kingdoms**. In 1959 the American biologist R H Whittaker proposed a five-kingdom system of classification. Later, in 1988, L Margulis and K V Schwartz built upon this classificatory framework and suggested the following five kingdoms should be recognised:

Prokaryotae
Protoctista
Fungi
Plantae
Animalia

A diagrammatic representation, or **cladogram**, of the evolutionary relationships between these kingdoms is shown in Figure 1. Although each kingdom is represented by many contemporary species, the Prokaryotae is the most primitive, first appearing at a relatively early stage in evolutionary development. Conversely, the Plantae, Fungi and Animalia are the most advanced. They first appeared at a much later stage in evolution. Furthermore, they all arose from a common group of organisms, the Protoctista, but have subsequently evolved over many millions of years as distinct groups.

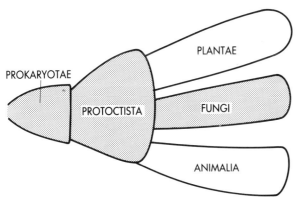

Figure 1   An outline of the 5-kingdom system of classification. Shading indicates the kingdoms that contain micro-organisms.

1.1 'MICRO-ORGANISMS'

The term '**micro-organism**', originally applied to any small organism that could not be seen clearly without the aid of a microscope, now means different things to different people. At best, only a descriptive and never a scientific term, there is current confusion over its application to the viruses. This important group, traditionally known as 'micro-organisms' because of their small size, chemical composition and reactions with other organisms, do not feature in the five-kingdom classification. Strict adherents to that scheme do not regard them as living organisms, and so do not use the term 'micro-organism' when referring to them. Fortunately, no one doubts that the term micro-organism applies to all the Prokaryotae, or bacteria, both photosynthetic and non-photosynthetic types. Elsewhere, among the more evolutionarily advanced kingdoms, the term is applied more loosely and less specifically. For instance, in the Protoctista it is applied to all unicellular, heterotrophic organisms, collectively known as protozoans, and to many unicellular and filamentous algae. Larger algae, however, such as 'seaweeds' are often excluded, even though they belong to the same taxonomic group. Among the fungi, the zygomycetes (e.g. moulds) and ascomycetes (e.g. yeasts) are clearly 'micro-organisms', but no one is absolutely certain about the status of basidiomycetes (e.g. mushrooms), which have microscopic hyphae, yet produce large, conspicuous fruiting bodies. Biologists therefore find themselves in something of a dilemma. Should the term 'micro-organism' be dropped, because it is imprecise; or should it be retained, because it has been used for many years and has become part of the vocabulary of non-specialists? There is no obvious solution. Suffice to say that throughout this book the term 'micro-organism' is applied to viruses, Prokaryotae, and all organisms that are classified within the kingdoms Protoctista and Fungi, regardless of their size. **Microbiology**, a term originally coined to describe the scientific study of micro-organisms, is also used in its broadest sense, to describe the biology of these four groups.

1.2 VIRUSES

Virology, the study of viruses, is the youngest branch of microbiology. It was not until the 1940s that microbiologists first saw viruses, when technical advances improved the resolution of electron microscopes. All viruses are intracellular parasites, ranging in diameter from 20–300 nm. Once inside their host cells they possess the ability to reproduce (replicate), but they cannot carry out any of the other activities that are characteristic of living organisms, namely growth, respiration, excretion, locomotion, feeding and response to stimuli. Although viruses do not have a cellular structure, they nevertheless consist mainly of nucleoproteins. This appears to give them some affinity to living organisms, because nucleoproteins are a major component of chromosomes in all the kingdoms that have evolved from the Prokaryotae. More specifically, all viruses have the following features:

(i) A central core of nucleic acid, either deoxyribonucleic acid (DNA) – in DNA viruses – or ribonucleic acid (RNA) – in RNA viruses.

(ii) A protein coat, or **capsid**, composed of individual protein elements called **capsomeres**.

(iii) Genes for transferring viral nucleic acid to the chromosome(s) of its host.

(iv) The ability to multiply in its host, by taking over the host cell's machinery for synthesising nucleic acids and proteins.

In addition, (v) some viruses contain one or two enzymes and (vi) others are surrounded by an **envelope**, formed from carbohydrate or lipoprotein. The fact that viruses can multiply inside their host cells, yet are inert outside them has led to two views about their biological status. A few biologists still regard them as exceptionally simple living organisms, representing an intermediate stage in the evolution of the animate from the inanimate. Most, however, believe they have originated in some way from the genetic material of living organisms, possibly by detachment of a small piece of nucleic acid that became surrounded by a protective coat of protein.

Viruses can be subdivided according to their host range, and possible origins, into three main classes: **animal viruses**, **plant viruses** and **bacterial viruses (bacteriophages)**. Another classification distinguishes between **DNA** and **RNA viruses**. Beyond that, classification is based on polyhedral, cylindrical or complex symmetry. Adenovirus, for example, a naked polyhedral type that infects the adenoids and tonsils, is an icosahedron. This means it has 20 faces, each face being an equilateral triangle. Herpes virus, the cause of cold sores, is similar, but surrounded by a spiked envelope. The most complex viruses are some bacteriophages. They have an icosahedral head, containing DNA, and a helical tail. Around the top of the tail is a collar. At its base is a tail plate, from which six long tail fibres project.

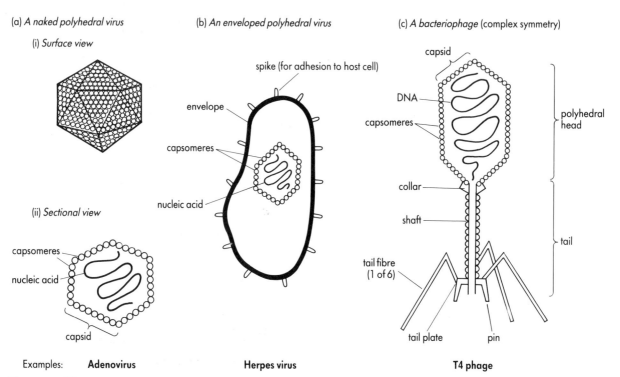

(a) *A naked polyhedral virus*

(i) *Surface view*

(ii) *Sectional view*

capsomeres

nucleic acid

capsid

Examples: **Adenovirus**

(b) *An enveloped polyhedral virus*

spike (for adhesion to host cell)

envelope

capsomeres

nucleic acid

Herpes virus

(c) *A bacteriophage* (complex symmetry)

capsid

DNA

capsomeres

polyhedral head

collar

shaft

tail

tail fibre (1 of 6)

tail plate   pin

tail

T4 phage

Figure 2   Viruses

(a) Based on host range

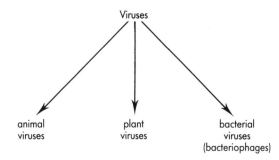

(b) Based on nucleic acid content and symmetry

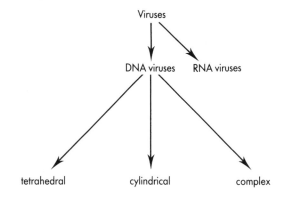

Figure 3   Schemes for classifying viruses

When a bacteriophage attacks a cell, one of two outcomes is possible. Firstly, the virus may multiply rapidly within the cell and destroy it. This is called **lysis** (Figure 4) because the host cell wall breaks down to release the new viruses. Alternatively, the virus may incorporate its DNA into the host cell's DNA and replicate, generation after generation, as part of the host cell's genome. Such a state is called **lysogeny** (Figure 5). Eventually, however, this incorporated phage DNA may initiate a **lytic cycle**, or viral life cycle.

The best understood viral life cycles, are those of the DNA-containing bacteriophages (phages) such as the so-called T-even phages (T2, T4, T6), parasitic in the cells of the bacterium *E. coli*. Stages in the lytic cycle of a T-phage are shown in Figure 4. An attack, or parasitisation, begins when a phage attaches to the bacterial cell wall, perforates it, and proceeds to inject its DNA. This injected DNA contains all the genetic information needed to take over the bacterial cell and convert it into a factory for the manufacture of more phages. The phage DNA inactivates bacterial DNA, and may eventually cause the bacterial chromosome to break down. Before this happens, however, phage DNA is replicated many hundreds of times, by causing the host cell to make the enzymes necessary for its own

(a) Adsorption to cell surface

(b) Penetration of viral DNA by injection

(c) Biosynthesis of viral DNA and capsids

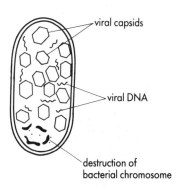

(d) Assembly of viral nucleic acid within each capsid

(e) Lysis of host cell; release of new phages

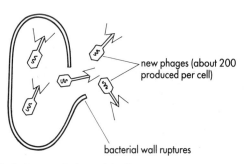

Lysis destroys the bacterial cell

Figure 4   Lysis – the lytic cycle of a T-even bacteriophage. Completion takes about 20 minutes

7

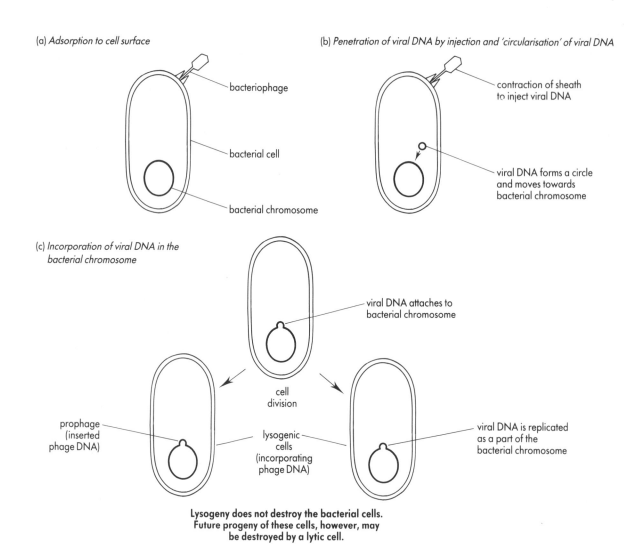

(a) *Adsorption to cell surface*

bacteriophage

bacterial cell

bacterial chromosome

(b) *Penetration of viral DNA by injection and 'circularisation' of viral DNA*

contraction of sheath to inject viral DNA

viral DNA forms a circle and moves towards bacterial chromosome

(c) *Incorporation of viral DNA in the bacterial chromosome*

viral DNA attaches to bacterial chromosome

cell division

prophage (inserted phage DNA)

lysogenic cells (incorporating phage DNA)

viral DNA is replicated as a part of the bacterial chromosome

Lysogeny does not destroy the bacterial cells. Future progeny of these cells, however, may be destroyed by a lytic cell.

Figure 5   Lysogeny – phage DNA inserts and replicates as part of a bacterial chromosome (This process does not occur in the T-even phages)

Adenovirus

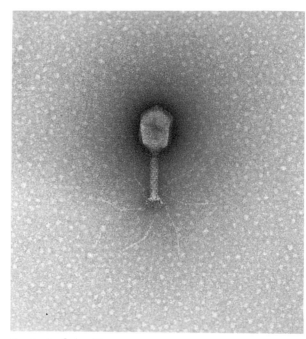

Bacteriophage T₄

replication. At the same time, the virus takes over cell protein synthesis, again causing the host cell to make its own viral proteins. Finally, in the cytoplasm of the host cell, the two components of a phage – its DNA and protein coat – come together and are assembled by enzymes to produce phages of the next generation. When this stage is complete, the bacterial cell dies. Its wall is lysed (or broken down) to release the newly formed phages.

Viral parasitisation by phages is not typical of all viral infections. In many cases the entire virus penetrates the host cell membrane, before its coat disintegrates and its nuclei acid passes to the cell nucleus. **Retroviruses**, including the virus that causes AIDS, contain RNA. Once inside its host, this RNA serves as a template for the formation of single-stranded DNA. This molecule, in turn, acts as a template for the formation of double-stranded DNA, which attaches to a host cell chromosome. Here, among other functions, it produces viral RNA for retroviruses of the next generation.

1.*3* PROKARYOTAE

The Prokaryotae, or **bacteria**, are very small (0.2 – 2.0 μm in diameter), relatively simple, single-celled micro-organisms. The kingdom includes both autotrophic and heterotrophic forms. All the bacteria lack nuclei organised within membranes. They also have no membrane-bound organelles or functional cytoplasmic units, such as centrioles. A gelatinous **capsule**, or **glycocalyx**, formed from polysaccharides, polypeptides, or both, surrounds a **cell wall**. The capsule helps the cell to adhere to surfaces, protects it from attack in parasitic forms, and probably conserves water. Motile bacteria have a **flagellum** (or several flagella) at one end, supported by a single central rod of the protein **flagellin**. Additional thread-like projections, looking like short flagella, are called **pili**. These serve to assist adhesion and join two bacteria together prior to the exchange of genetic material. Bacterial DNA is present in two locations. Firstly, in the **circular chromosome**, believed to be anchored to a folded part of the cell membrane called the **mesosome**, and in much smaller, unattached circular units, the **plasmids**. These carry genes that the bacterium may need on special occasions, such as those for antibiotic resistance (R-factors) or for conjugation (F-factors). Proteins are synthesised at the bacterial **ribosomes**, in the cytoplasm. Storage products such as polyphosphate granules, glycogen or starch occur throughout the cytoplasm in **inclusion granules**.

The classification of bacteria presents particular difficulties, because species that are totally unrelated bear a close physical resemblance to one another. Hans Christian Gram, a Danish Biologist, made the first taxonomically valid classification in 1884, on the basis of cell wall reactions to dyes. After spreading the bacteria on a microscope slide, a mixture of crystal violet and iodine solution was added. This was followed by washing in 95% alcohol (ethanol), then a second staining with safranin. **Gram-positive bacteria** stained purple, whereas **gram-negative bacteria** stained red.

An alternative classification uses shape as the principal criterion. Bacteria may be spherical (**cocci**), rod-shaped (**bacilli**), shaped like a cork-screw (**spirilla**), comma-like (**vibrio**), or filamentous. Further differentiation is often possible according to the way in which bacteria tend to be grouped, especially after cell division. For instance, *Diplococci* occur in pairs, *Streptococci* form chains and *Staphylococci* are grouped into clusters, like bunches of grapes. The filamentous bacteria are of particular interest because most are photosynthetic. This group, formerly called blue-green algae because of their superficial resemblance to filamentous green algae, are now known as **Cyanobacteria** (see page 0 and 0).

A third system of classification, dating from the 1960s, is based on the structure of the bacterial ribosome (16S-RNA). Two major groups are recognised:

(i) **Archaebacteria**, the most primitive group, with mostly proteins and no peptidoglycan in their walls, and

(ii) **Eubacteria**, more recently evolved, with peptidoglycan as their principal wall component.

Archaebacteria comprise methanogens, which give off methane, thermoacidophiles, which can live in hot springs, and halobacteria, the occupants of very salty environments. Eubacteria are more widespread and generally less exotic, found in water, soil or living in association with other organisms.

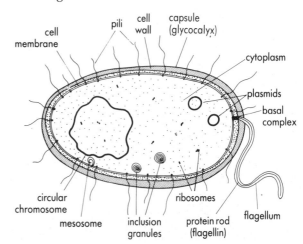

Figure 6   The generalised structure of a bacterium

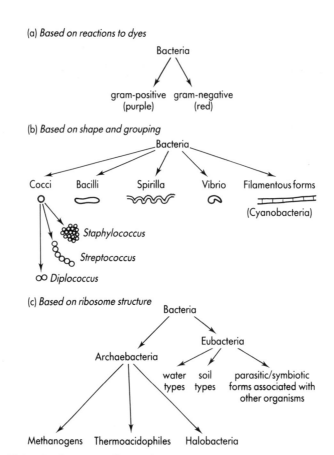

(a) *Based on reactions to dyes*

(b) *Based on shape and grouping*

(c) *Based on ribosome structure*

Figure 7   Schemes for classifying Prokaryotae (bacteria)

Table 1   Some features of gram-positive and gram-negative bacteria

FEATURE	GRAM-POSITIVE BACTERIA	GRAM-NEGATIVE BACTERIA
Response of Grams's stain	stain purple	stain red
Cell wall components	mostly polysaccharides, with a little lipid and protein	polysaccharides with more lipid (20%) and protein
Flagella		May be inserted at one or both ends of bacilli
Endospores	produced during unfavourable conditions by some species	not produced
Response to lysozyme	dissolves cell wall, causing bacteria to swell by osmosis and burst	
Examples	*Staphylococcus aureus* *Bacillus subtilis* *Lactobacillus bulgaricus*	*Escherichia coli* *Acetobacter aceti* *Agrobacterium tumefaciens*

The life cycle of a bacterium often involves nothing more than vegetative growth and cell division. Typically, after growing to its maximum size, the rod-shaped *Bacillus subtilis*, a saprophytic fresh-water species, divides longitudinally into two daughter cells. This cell division begins with replication of the circular chromosome. The cell then elongates to separate the two chromosomes, before a cross wall forms to divide this elongated cell into two. Under unfavourable conditions, notable high temperatures or the presence of toxins, this bacterium may enter a state of suspended animation. It does this by forming an **endospore**, a thick-walled protective resting stage, which bursts open to resume growth as soon as favourable conditions return.

Studies of the bacillus *Escherichia coli*, a species found in the human intestine, have shown that during its life cycle it may receive additional DNA from three different sources, by processes known as transformation, transduction and conjugation.

(i) **Transformation** involves the uptake of naked DNA and its incorporation into the bacterial chromosome. The naked DNA, generally released into the environment when a neighbouring bacterium dies and decomposes, is taken up as a single strand

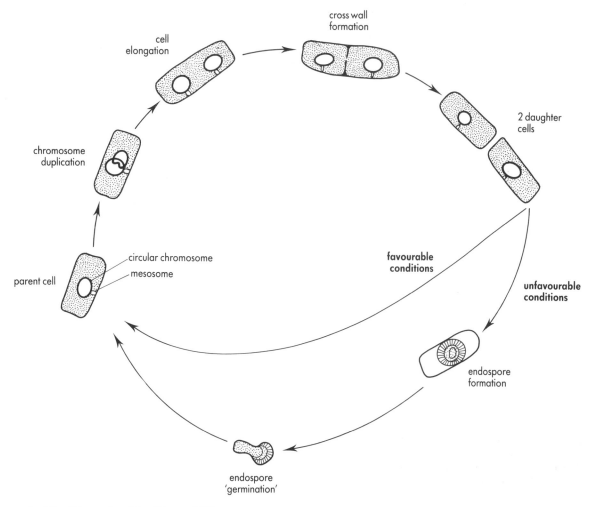

Figure 8   The life-cycle of Bacillus subtilis

(Figure 9a). The incorporation of this additional DNA into the bacterial chromosome may result in the displacement of some other genes.

(ii) **Transduction** occurs when a bacteriophage transfers DNA from one bacterium to another. The bacteriophage acts as a DNA vector, often transferring DNA from a bacterium on which its attack was lethal to one that was resistant.

(iii) **Conjugation** takes place between two different strains of a bacterium known as F^+ and F^-. The F^+ strain has genes for the F (fertility) factor; the F^- strain has none. This F factor may be present in a cell, either as part of the bacterial chromosome, or, more likely, a part of a plasmid. F factor-carrying plasmids can replicate within the cells that contain them. Conjugation begins when a F^+ bacterium produces a conjugation tube formed from a large pilus called a sex pilus. The F^+ factor, either in

E. coli *bacteria*

naked DNA enters
from the environment

DNA enters via a
bacteriophage, acting
as a vector

DNA enters, via a
conjugation tube, from
another bacterium

Figure 9   Transformation, transduction and conjugation in E. coli

the form of an uncoiled plasmid or part of the chromosomal DNA, passes through the tube and into the F^- bacterium. Here, as a plasmid or part of a chromosome, it transforms the F^- bacterium into F^+.

The filamentous cyanobacterium *Anabaena* grows abundantly wherever there is warmth, light and moisture. For instance, in the rice fields of the tropical and sub-tropical regions it often forms a blue-green surface mat. In the UK, its common name is 'moon spit', because of the gelatinous, bubbly nature of colonies that suddenly appear at the surface of ponds in summer. *Anabaena* is a colonial species consisting of straight or curved chains of dark green **vegetative cells**, in which photosynthesis takes place. Between these cells, spaced irregularly, are larger, thick-walled, colourless cells, the '**heterocysts**', where nitrogen fixation occurs (see section 2.5). The heavy walls of the 'heterocysts' prevent oxygen from entering and inactivating the nitrogen-fixing enzymes, notably **nitrogenase**.

At both ends of 'heterocysts', where they border vegetative cells, are thickened regions called **peg projections**. These are effective in keeping out oxygen and in passing on the products of nitrogen fixation to vegetative cells. Each vegetative cell is bounded by a wall of mucoprotein (polysaccharides + protein), covered by a thick, slimy mucilaginous sheath. Attached to the cell membrane are many folded photosynthetic membranes, called **thylakoids**. They contain the photosynthetic pigments chlorophyll and carotenoids. Scattered between them are spherical sacs, or **phycobilisomes**, which contain accessory photosynthetic pigments. Elsewhere throughout

the peripheral cytoplasm there are some **ribosomes**, for protein synthesis, droplets of stored **lipids**, and **gas vacuoles** giving buoyancy. At the centre of the cell is a loop of DNA. Reproduction takes place by fragmentation of the filament or by 'spore' formation. The 'spores' are thick-walled vegetative cells (also called 'heterocysts'), with little, if any, photosynthetic activity. At the end of the growing season the 'spores' may break away, survive unfavourable conditions, and 'germinate' when favourable conditions return.

Anabaena circinalis

(a) Filament

'heterocyst'   mucilagenous sheath

vegetative cells

(b) Vegatative cells and 'heterocyst'

mucilagenous sheath   'heterocyst'   vegetative cell

cell wall
cell membrane

loop of DNA
ribosomes

gas vacuole

thylakoid   phycobilisomes

oil globules

thick cell wall (polysaccharides + proteins)

peg projection

Figure 10   Anabena

1.4 PROTOCTISTA

Protoctists are unicellular organisms or assemblages of relatively unspecialised similar cells. The kingdom includes organisms that were formerly classified as protozoa, algae and slime moulds. All have a true nucleus, surrounded by a nuclear envelope. They also have membrane-bound organelles and a 9 + 2 array of microfilaments in their cilia and flagella. For these reasons, they are grouped with plants, fungi and animals as **eukaryotes** to distinguish them from the bacteria, (**prokaryotes**).

Table 2 summarises the differences between prokaryotes and eukaryotes. Protoctists are neither plants, fungi nor animals. The Margulis and Schwartz classification places each of the four groups that traditionally were classes of the phylum protozoa into the 'phylum' taxon. It also places *Phytophthora*, the late blight of potatoes, in this kingdom rather than among the fungi.

The following classification scheme of protoctista, selected to include species that have been studied in schools, has been compiled by a joint working party of the Association for Science Education and the Institute of Biology.

Phylum – **Rhizopoda** (rhizopods)
  Organisms equipped with pseudopodia for locomotion.
  Example: *Amoeba*
Phylum – **Zoomastigina** (flagellates)
  Heterotrophic organisms equipped with at least one flagellum for locomotion.
  Example: *Trypanosoma*
Phylum – **Apicomplexa** (sporozoans)
  Organisms, mainly parasitic, with multiple fission stages in their life history.
  Example: *Plasmodium*
Phylum – **Ciliophora** (ciliates)
  Organisms, attached or motile, with surface cilia.
  Example: *Paramecium*
Phylum – **Euglenophyta** (euglenoid flagellates)
  A group with photosynthetic and non-photosynthetic members. Flagellate, with their own distinctive biochemistry.
  Example: *Euglena*
Phylum – **Oomycota** (oomycetes)
  A group which reproduces sexually by fertilisation of male and female gametangia; asexual sporangia produce biflagellate spores; hypae non-septate (no cross walls).
  Example: *Phytophthora*
Phylum – **Chlorophyta** (green algae)
  Photosynthetic, with essentially the same pigments as plants, unicellular, colonial and filamentous.
  Example: *Chlamydomonas*
Phylum – **Rhodophyta** (red algae)
  Photosynthetic, with plastids containing red pigments as well as chlorophyll.
  Example: *Chondrus*
Phylum – **Phaeophyta** (brown algae)
  Photosynthetic, with plastids containing brown pigments as well as chlorophyll.
  Example: *Fucus*

Table 2 Some characteristic features of prokaryotic and eukaryotic cells

	PROKARYOTIC CELLS	EUKARYOTIC CELLS
GENERAL	small (1-10 μm long)	large (10-30 μm long)
	bounded by a cell wall formed mostly from peptidoglycan	cell wall, if present, formed mostly from cellulose (plants)
	functional ribosomes free in cytoplasm	functional ribosomes attached to rough endoplasmic reticulum
	flagella, when present, supported by a single rod of protein (flagellin)	flagella, when present, supported by 9 + 2 microtubules of protein (tubulin)
	cells divide by fission (splitting); no mitosis or meiosis	cell division usually involves mitosis, but may also be meiotic
DNA	single-stranded, not associated with proteins, and present as one circular chromosome	double-stranded, complexed with histone proteins, and dispersed throughout several rod-like (linear) chromosomes
	smaller circles of DNA (plasmids) may also be present	no plasmids
NUCLEUS	absent	present, bounded by a double nuclear membrane, which encloses the chromosomes and a nucleolus, where ribosomes are synthesised
ORGANELLES	absent	in addition to the nucleus, mitochondria, rough and smooth endoplasmic reticulum, Golgi apparatus, plastids (plants) and lysosomes are typical cell inclusions

Figure 11 illustrates one species from each of the first four phyla listed above. Most of the species classified in these groups are unicellular and heterotrophic. Free-living representatives occur in fresh water, the sea and damp places on land. Parasitic types occur mostly in the body fluids of invertebrates and vertebrates. *Plasmodium*, the cause of malaria, and *Trypanosoma*, the cause of sleeping sickness, have considerable economic importance.

The phylum Chlorophyta includes all the green algae. Those that belong to the genus *Chlorella* occur in several different habitats, namely in fresh water, brackish water and moist soil. Some species are symbiotic. *C. lichinia*, for example, is an algae symbiont of the lichen *Calicium chlorina*, while *Zoochorella* grows as a symbiont in *Hydra*. All members of the genus are non-motile and unicellular. The individual cells of *Chlorella* are spherical, subspherical or ellipsoidal, bounded by a wall of cellulose. Each cell has a cup-shaped chloroplast, in which the chlorophyll-containing membranes (thylakoids) lack grana-like organisation. Crystalline protein bodies, called **pyrenoids**, sometimes surrounded by stored starch grains, may occur in the chloroplast. A single nucleus, together with mitochondria and Golgi bodies occur in the cytoplasm, which may lie mostly within the cavity of the chloroplast, or to one side of it. Under conditions that are favourable for its growth, *Chlorella* reproduces exclusively by the formation of (normally four) **autospores**. Two successive divisions occur within the cell wall of a mother cell. The autospores are released when the mother cell's cell wall gelatinises or ruptures (Figure 12b).

As *Chlorella* occasionally fouls swimming pools, lakes and canals, biologists have for many years used algicides such as copper sulphate to control the organism. More recently, though, biologists have begun to view it in a more favourable light. Biochemical analysis of its cells has shown that they contain about 50% protein, 20% carbohydrate and 20% fat, with significant amounts of amino acids, vitamins and minerals. Following from negative toxicity tests, research is currently underway to investigate the feasibility of growing *Chlorella* in mass culture for use as human food or animal feed. Another future use may well be in controlling sewage disposal. *Chlorella* grows and multiplies in raw sewage, liberating oxygen into its surroundings, thereby creating conditions that favour the growth of aerobic sewage-degrading bacteria and fungi. Looking further ahead, another possibility is the use of this fast-growing, photosynthetic organism in the regulation of oxygen and carbon dioxide levels inside space vehicles designed to carry astronauts.

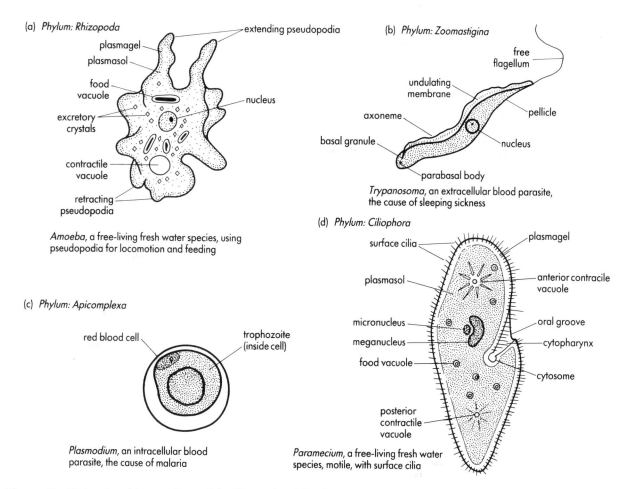

(a) *Phylum: Rhizopoda*

extending pseudopodia

plasmagel

plasmasol

food vacuole

excretory crystals

nucleus

contractile vacuole

retracting pseudopodia

Amoeba, a free-living fresh water species, using pseudopodia for locomotion and feeding

(b) *Phylum: Zoomastigina*

free flagellum

undulating membrane

axoneme

basal granule

pellicle

nucleus

parabasal body

Trypanosoma, an extracellular blood parasite, the cause of sleeping sickness

(c) *Phylum: Apicomplexa*

red blood cell

trophozoite (inside cell)

Plasmodium, an intracellular blood parasite, the cause of malaria

(d) *Phylum: Ciliophora*

surface cilia

plasmagel

plasmasol

anterior contracile vacuole

micronucleus

meganucleus

food vacuole

oral groove

cytopharynx

cytosome

posterior contractile vacuole

Paramecium, a free-living fresh water species, motile, with surface cilia

Figure 11   Heterotrophic members of the Protoctista kingdom

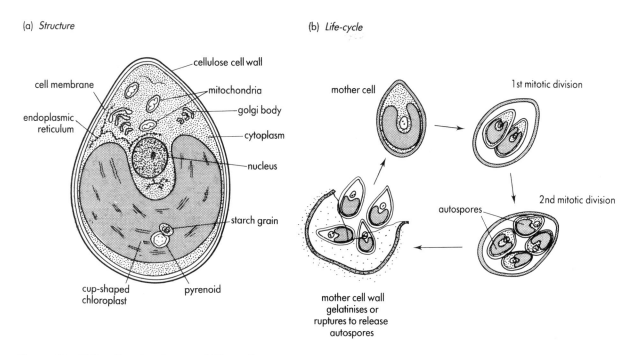

(a) *Structure*

cellulose cell wall

cell membrane

mitochondria

endoplasmic reticulum

golgi body

cytoplasm

nucleus

starch grain

cup-shaped chloroplast

pyrenoid

(b) *Life-cycle*

mother cell

1st mitotic division

2nd mitotic division

autospores

mother cell wall gelatinises or ruptures to release autospores

Figure 12   Chlorella: *structure and life-cycle*

1.5 FUNGI

The Fungi kingdom consists of eukaryotic heterotrophs, feeding as saprophytes, parasites and symbionts. The basic structural unit of a fungus is a multinucleate **hypha**. Nutrients are obtained by absorbing soluble organic and inorganic material into the hyphae. Each hypha is surrounded by a protective wall, with chitin, not cellulose, as a major wall component. No fungus contains chlorophyll, so none are photosynthetic. Asexual and sexual reproduction often results in the formation of **non-motile spores**. There are three phyla – the **Zygomycota** (zygomycetes), **Ascomycota** (ascomycetes) and **Basidiomycota** (basidiomycetes). This classification is based on differences in sexual reproduction and on the nature of the hyphae, illustrated in Figure 13.

(a) *Generalised structure*

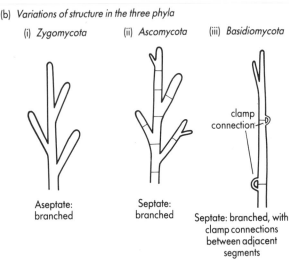

(b) *Variations of structure in the three phyla*

(i) *Zygomycota* — Aseptate: branched

(ii) *Ascomycota* — Septate: branched

(iii) *Basidiomycota* — clamp connection — Septate: branched, with clamp connections between adjacent segments

Figure 13   Fungal hyphae

1.5.1 Zygomycota

The fungi included in this phylum have non-septate hyphae. Their sexual reproduction is by **gametangia** producing **zygospore**. *Mucor hiemalis*, the common bread mould, is a saprophytic zygomycete, the cause of food-spoilage in bread and other moist carbohydrate-containing food products. The branched, multinucleate feeding hyphae of this fungus are of two mating strains, plus (+) and minus (−). All the nuclei are haploid (n). Both strains reproduce asexually by producing spores in aeriel, roughly spherical **sporangia**, carried at the tips of long supporting stalks, or **sporangiophores**. If both + and − strains are present in a colony, their nuclei may fuse to form a zygote, the only diploid (2n) phase in the life-cycle. Zygote formation results from the fusion of two equal sized gametangia, each with several nuclei. The two gametangia are cut off from other parts of the hypha by complete cross walls. After the tips of the gametangia have broken down, the nuclei of + and − strains fuse in pairs to form zygotes. A thick, resistant wall develops around all the zygotes, forming a resting, overwintering stage in the cycle called a **zygospore**. On the return of favourable conditions, the zygospore germinates to produce a single sporangium at the tip of a sporangiophore. The spores in this sporangium are the products of meiosis. Each zygote (2n) in the zygospore undergoes meiosis to produce four spores, two plus (+) and two minus (−). Meiotic divisions of all the zygotes produces anything from 40–100 haploid spores, which move from the zygospore into the sporangium as it develops.

1.5.2 Ascomycota

Ascomycetes have septate hyphae. Their reproduction involves spore production inside a container, the **ascus**.

The **yeasts** are unicellular ascomycetes, which have evolved from hypha-forming ancestors. Three species, possibly different from one another by no more than a single gene, are of economic importance:

   (i) *Saccharomyces cerevisiae* – the yeast of brewing and baking.
   (ii) *Saccharomyces ellipsoideus* – the yeast of wine.
   (iii) *Saccharomyces carlsbergensis* – the yeast of lager.

Individual yeast cells are ellipsoidal-spherical, encased in a rigid, permeable cell wall composed largely of mannose and glucose polymers. Cell organelles include mitochondria, Golgi bodies and a nucleus. There is an extensive endoplasmic reticulum, extending throughout the cytoplasm. One or more large vacuoles occupy a central position in the cell. Storage materials, notably glycogen granules and oil globules in the cytoplasm, with polyphosphate granules in the vacuole, may be present. The life-cycle (Figure 15) involves an alteration of generations between diploid (2n) and haploid (n) phases. Under conditions that are unfavourable for growth, the diploid vegetative cells undergo meiosis, to form

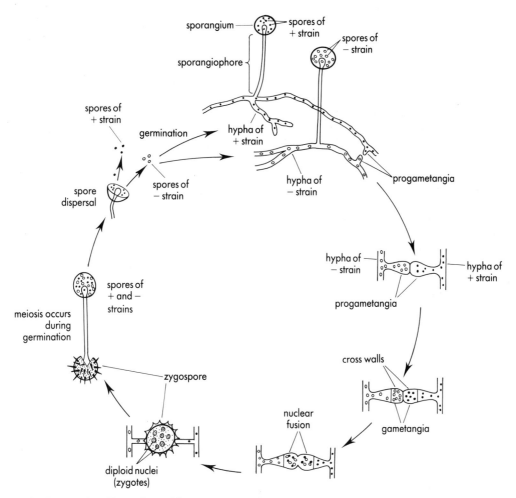

Figure 14 **The life-cycle of bread mould (Mucor hiemalis)**

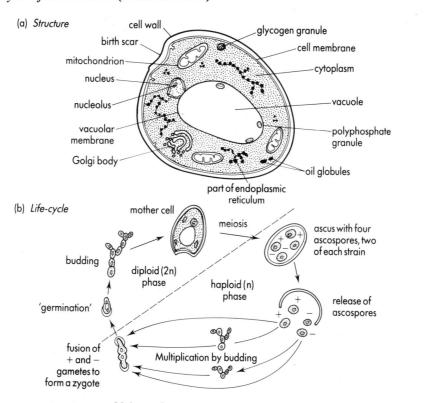

Figure 15 **Saccharomyces: *structure and life-cycle***

an ascus with four haploid ascospores. These are of different mating strains, two plus (+) and two minus (−). Each ascospore can behave as a gamete, fusing with another of a different strain to form a zygote, from which the next generation of diploid cells is budded. As Figure 15 shows, both the diploid and haploid cells are capable of reproducing asexually by budding.

Yeast is a 'facultative anaerobe'; that is, it is capable of respiring both aerobically (when it develops mitochondria) and anaerobically (when it doesn't) depending on the availability of oxygen. Anaerobic respiration, or **fermentation**, uses glucose as respirable substrate and results in the production of alcohol (ethanol) and carbon dioxide. Used for centuries in baking, brewing and wine-making, yeasts have recently become very important organisms in genetic research and biotechnology (see section 3.3.3).

The grey-green mould *Penicillium notatum* bears a superficial resemblance to *Mucor*, and grows on similar substrates such as bread, cheese or fruit. Even so, unlike the bread mould, it has septate hyphae and is therefore classified as an ascomycete. *Penicillium*, source of the antibiotic penicillin, has feeding hyphae, which divide into branches through its substrate, and aeriel hyphae called **condiophores** that branch dichotomously at their upper ends to form **sterigma**. From the tips of these sterigma, naked cytoplasm oozes, rounds off, and then hardens to form chains of grey-green conidiospores. Following dispersal by air currents to a suitable substratum, each condiospore germinates to form a hypha. *Penicillium* lacks a method of sexual reproduction.

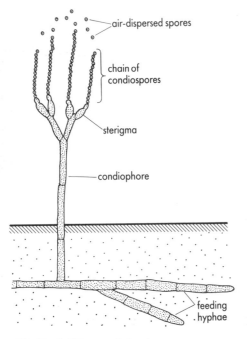

Figure 16   **Penicillium notatum**

1.5.3 Basidiomycota

Fungi classified as basidiomycetes have septate walls. Their sexual reproduction involves spores produced externally on a **basidium**.

The field mushroom (*Agaricus campestris*) is a fleshy, edible basidiomycete, found in grassy meadows with a high organic content. A mushroom's fruiting body, or **basidiocarp**, consists of a cap, the **pileus**, supported by a stalk, the **stipe**. On the underside of the cap are radially arranged gills, lined by spore-producing basidia. The diploid nucleus of each basidium undergoes meiosis to form four **basidiospores**. Again, as in yeast, these are of two different strains, two plus (+) and two minus (−). On germinating, the basidiospores produce a **primary mycelium** formed either from a + or a − hypha. Ultimately, fusion between the two types of hypha produces a **secondary mycelium**, with two nuclei per segment, one of each type. These segments have a characteristic structure, with the formation of swellings called clamp connections around each cross wall. Basidiocarps develop from dense wefts (interlacing threads) of hyphae of the secondary mycelium.

Commercial production of the cultivated mushroom *A. bisporus* is carried out in mushroom houses equipped to control temperature, humidity and aeration. Modern commercial mushroom production has three preparatory stages: **composting**, **'spawning'** and **casing**. The mushrooms are usually grown in wooden boxes, stacked one above another in tiers of 3 or 4. The most widely favoured substrate is composted wheat straw, fermented by adding horse, pig or poultry manure. By stacking straw-manure mixtures in long narrow piles, about 1 m high and 1.8 m wide, which are regularly aerated by turning, a rapid rise in temperature to 60-80°C is achieved. This, in effect, acts as a form of pasteurisation, killing off any foreign fungal spores, mites, insects and nematodes in the compost. After 3–4 weeks, when the temperature has cooled to around 20°C, the compost is tightly packed into sterilised boxes and 'spawned' with a pure inoculum of *A. bisporus*. The 'spawn' is produced by growing the fungus on sterilised wheat or rye grains with added chalk to maintain alkalinity.

After the 'spawn' has been mixed with compost, its fungal hyphae spread throughout each box, covering the compost with a white weft of hyphae, smelling strongly of mushrooms. After 10–15 days at 25–28°C, the boxes are cased with a 2–3 cm depth of casing soil, added to induce the formation of fruiting bodies. In the UK, peat mixed with granular chalk is often used for casing. This mixture favours the growth of the bacterium *Pseudomonas putica*, which in some obscure way

THE LIBRARY
GUILDFORD COLLEGE
of Further and Higher Education

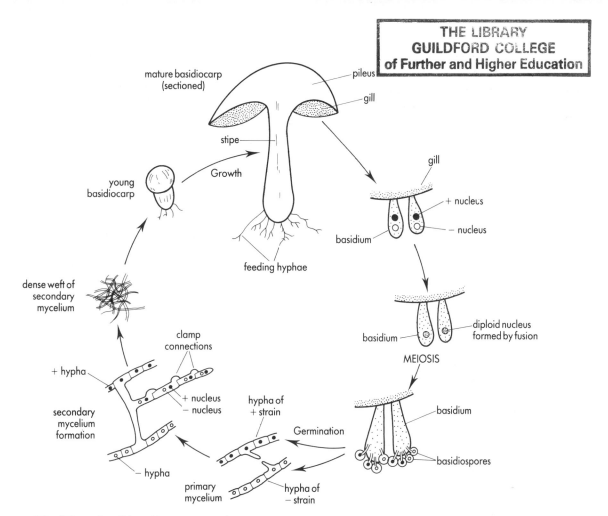

Figure 17   The life-cycle of Agaricus campestris

Commercial mushroom production

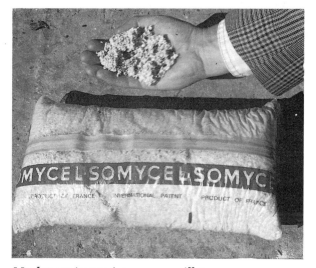

Mushroom 'spawn', grown on millet

– possibly by removing inhibitors from the compost or by releasing ferrous iron – triggers the production of fruiting bodies from dense clusters of hyphae. Fruiting body formation is favoured by high humidity (95%) and relatively low temperature (15–17°C). Approximately 18–25 days after casing the first crop is ready for picking. Successive flushes of fruiting bodies appear over the next 30–40 days, providing all the mature fruiting bodies are removed and the compost is kept moist by watering.

QUESTIONS

1 The diagram below illustrates a virus.

a) Label the parts A-G.
b) Which group or organisms is parasitised by this virus?
c) Name the nucleic acid that the virus carries in its head.
d) What term is used to describe the symmetry of this virus?
e) Cells attacked by this virus may undergo *lysis* or *lysogeny*. Explain how these processes differ.

2 Match the following characteristics of viruses, bacteria or fungi with their functions:

Characteristics	Function
a) Mesosomes	cell wall synthesis
b) Cell membrane	ribosomal RNA synthesis
c) Mitochondria	ATP production
d) Vacuole	stored carbohydrate
e) Golgi apparatus	transfer of genetic material
f) Axial filament	stored water
g) Lysosome	motility
h) Capsid	lysozyme secretion
i) Nuclear envelope	selective permeability
j) Cell wall	stored digestive enzymes
k) Pili	maintains cell shape
l) Glycogen granule	encloses DNA or RNA
m) Bacteriophage tail	encloses chromosomes
n) Nucleolus	adherence to other cells

3 Critically evaluate the term 'micro-organism', with particular reference to the viruses.
How are 'micro-organisms' classified within the 5-kingdom system?
Do you consider that the merits of this system outweigh its shortcomings?

4 By reference to a named bacterium and fungus, explain the meaning of the terms 'prokaryotic' and 'eukaryotic'.
Draw up a table to list the most important diagnostic features of prokaryotic and eukaryotic cells.

5 Describe how you would distinguish between bacteria, algae and protozoa.
Why is *Anabaena*, formerly classified as a blue-green alga, now regarded as a bacterium?

6 Describe and justify the classification of fungi into three phyla (Zygomycota, Ascomycota and Basidiomycota).
Why is the late blight of potatoes (*Phytophtora infestans*) now classified as a Protoctistan?

7 Survey the commercial applications of algae and fungi.
How may algae and fungi cause economic losses?
What measures can be taken to control harmful algae and fungi?

BIBLIOGRAPHY

Micro-organisms: an introduction

Clegg, C J (1984) *Lower Plants* John Murray
Deverall, B (1981) *Fungal Parasitism* (Studies in Biology No. 17) Edward Arnold
Fay, P (1983) *The Blue-Greens* (Studies in Biology No. 160) Edward Arnold
Hudson, H J (1980) *Fungal Saprophytism* (Studies in Biology No. 32) Edward Arnold
Ingle, M R (1986) *Microbes and Biotechnology* (Studies in Advanced Biology No. 4) Blackwell
Ingold, C T (1961) *The Biology of Fungi* Hutchinson Educational
Institute of Biology, Association for Science Education (1989) *Biological Nomenclature* Institute of Biology
Kumar, H and Singh, H (1976) *A Textbook on Algae* The Macmillan Press
Margulis, L and Schwartz, K V (1988) *Five Kingdoms: An Illustrated Guide To The Phyla Of Life On Earth* 2nd Edn. Freeman and Co. New York
Sleigh, M A (1972) *The Biology of the Protozoa* Edward Arnold

MICRO-ORGANISMS IN ACTION

Viruses, and all living organisms, possess the ability to increase their numbers through reproduction. In addition, all other living micro-organisms feed, respire, grow, excrete, move and respond to stimuli. Biologists are currently showing great interest in micro-organisms because of their growth rates and metabolic activities. In a hungry world, where many are starving, new food sources offer new hope. Many micro-organisms can double their biomass in hours or days, whereas the more traditional foods, namely plants and animals, may take weeks, months or years. As they grow, micro-organisms synthesise an enormous number of complex organic molecules, they modify some of their products, and break down others. Increasingly, micro-organisms are being used to synthesise useful products, modify the structure of chemicals and break down harmful waste substances.

This exploitation of micro-organisms to enhance the quality of human life owes its current boom to two technical advances. Firstly, new techniques in **gene manipulation** have made it possible for genes to be transferred from one organism to another. Used as recipients for foreign genes, the cells of certain bacteria and yeasts behave admirably, expressing the novel genes and secreting their products. Secondly, advances in **chemical engineering** have led to the production of stainless steel containers for the mass cultivation of micro-organisms, together with machinery for the extraction of their products. Taken together, these two technical advances provide a basis for new microbial products and processes, both in the immediate future and for many decades to come.

This exciting possibility, however, should not obscure the fact that micro-organisms can be harmful as well as beneficial. For instance, among bacteria that regulate the nitrogen cycle, there are some that fix nitrogen, making it available to crops, and others that break down nitrates, depriving crops of a nitrogen supply. More seriously, from a human viewpoint, some bacteria, protoctists and fungi are pathogens, causing infectious diseases in humans, farm animals and crops. **Biotechnology** is the exploitation of organisms in ways that benefit the human situation. It encompasses many of the diverse activities of micro-organisms, both good and bad.

2.1 NUTRITION

Described in terms of their nutritional requirements, micro-organisms are either autotrophs or heterotrophs.

Autotrophs
Autotrophs have the ability to synthesise all of their nutritional requirements from just three sources: carbon dioxide, a hydrogen donor, and mineral salts. Two types of autotroph, photoautotrophs and chemoautotrophs, are recognised.

Photoautotrophs use radiant energy from sunlight, absorbed and made available to the cell by photosynthetic pigments which act as intermediates. In the cyanobacteria and algae, as in higher plants, the hydrogen donor is water. Here, photosynthesis may be represented by the general equation:

$$2H_2O + CO_2 \xrightarrow[\text{chlorophyll}]{\text{light}} (CH_2O) + O_2 + H_2O$$

Photosynthetic bacteria such as *Chlorobium* and *Chromatium* do not use water as a hydrogen source. Neither do they release oxygen as a by-product. Instead, they oxidise hydrogen sulphide to sulphur, which is retained as granules within the cell cytoplasm:

$$2H_2S + CO_2 \rightarrow (CH_2O) + 2S + 2H_2O$$

Chemoautotrophs, the second group of autotrophic bacteria, use atmospheric oxygen to oxidise inorganic molecules. As a result of these oxidations, energy is released and then trapped by adenosine triphosphate (ATP), to drive synthetic processes in the cell.
Nitrosomonas, for example, oxidises ammonia to nitrites:

$$2NH_3 + 3O_2 \rightarrow 2HNO_2 + 2H_2O + \text{energy}$$

Nitrobacter oxidises nitrites to nitrates:
$$2HNO_2 + O \rightarrow HNO_3 + energy$$

Thiobacillus oxidises sulphur to sulphate:
$$2S + 3O_2 + 2H_2O \rightarrow 2H_2SO_4 + energy$$

Heterotrophs

Heterotrophs, by far the largest group of bacteria, together with all the fungi, must be supplied with complex organic molecules, such as carbohydrates, lipids and proteins. They obtain energy from the oxidation of these macromolecules into smaller, simpler compounds. Again, the energy released from these oxidations is utilised, via ATP, to drive cellular processes. Most heterotrophs feed as saprophytes, releasing enzymes into their environment and absorbing the soluble products of enzyme action. Some heterotrophic bacteria and fungi feed as **symbionts**, in close physiological association with other organisms, a relationship that gives benefit to both partners. Finally, a relatively small number of bacteria and fungi feed as **parasites**, obtaining their nutrients from a living organism of a different species. As a result of this relationship only the parasite benefits, while the host invariably suffers some degree of cell or tissue damage.

2.2 RESPIRATION

ATP is the immediate energy reservoir in any cell, and it can be tapped for growth, movement or any other activity. All organisms synthesise ATP during a series of oxidation-reduction reactions, known as biochemical pathways. These pathways may be divided into three major types, depending on the nature of the electron acceptors: aerobic respiration, anaerobic respiration and fermentation.

During **aerobic respiration** electrons, removed from a substrate molecule such as glucose, are shunted, in turn, along a chain of acceptors. The acceptors are reduced and reoxidised. Oxygen is the final electron acceptor in the chain. Water is the end product. Micro-organisms that can only synthesise their ATP in this way are called **obligate aerobes**, because they cannot live in the absence of oxygen.

Anaerobic respiration occurs in the absence of oxygen, but requires the presence of nitrates, sulphates or carbonates. These compounds substitute for oxygen as electron acceptors, and are subsequently reduced.

Fermentation not only occurs in the absence of oxygen, but also in the absence of any added electron acceptor. Reduced nicotine adenine dinucleotide (NADH) plays an important role in fermentation pathways, acting as a hydrogen donor. Yeasts cause the reaction:

Glucose pyruvate + NADH → ethanol + NAD
This is **alcoholic fermentation**. Conversely, some bacteria have enzymes that enable them to convert pyruvate into lactic acid:

Glucose pyruvate + NADH → lactic acid + NAD
This is **lactate fermentation**.

Other similar biochemical pathways in different species of bacteria end with the formation of a wide range of organic acids, alcohols and ketones. Micro-organisms that obtain their energy by anaerobic respiration or fermentation may be either obligate or facultative anaerobes. An **obligate anaerobe**, such as the bacterium *Clostridium*, which lives in the soil, may die in the presence of oxygen because one or more of its enzyme systems is inactivated. **Facultative anaerobes**, on the other hand, such as yeasts, are able to obtain energy either by aerobic respiration or by fermentation, and do not require oxygen for biosynthesis.

2.3 POPULATION GROWTH

Micro-organisms can be grown in the laboratory, either in liquid media, known as **broths**, or on **solid media**, hardened to a jelly-like consistency by adding agar. The nutritional requirements of photoautotrophs and heterotrophs are listed in Table 3. These essential nutrients are either added to a broth, or incorporated into a solid medium, depending on the micro-organism that is to be grown. Large conical flasks, fitted with cotton wool plugs or rubber bungs and glass tubes – so gas can escape – are suitable for small-scale broth cultures. Alternatively, many micro-organisms can be grown on solid-based media, contained in petri dishes. Rough estimates of growth rates can be made by regularly measuring the diameter of a bacterial or fungal colony, as it spreads from a central point to cover the surface of a solid growth medium (Figure 18). More accurate estimates of growth rate, however, are dependent on broth cultures. Unit samples are withdrawn at regular intervals, filtered, dried and weighed. Mass is then plotted against time to produce a growth curve.

Changes in cell density during population growth can be determined by two methods:
  (i) Total counts, of both living and dead cells, using a haemocytometer.
  (ii) Viable counts, of living cells, made by counting the number of colonies formed after serial dilution and plating onto a solid nutrient medium.

A **haemocytometer** (Figure 19), originally designed for counting blood cells, can also be used for counting cells of bacteria, yeasts or algae

Table 3 The nutritional requirements of micro-organisms feeding as photoautotrophs and heterotrophs

NUTRIENT	SOURCES REQUIRED BY PHOTO-AUTOTROPHS	SOURCES REQUIRED BY HETEROTROPHS
Carbon	carbon dioxide	carbohydrates amino acids peptides lipids
Nitrogen	ammonium (NH_4^+) ions nitrate (NO_3^-) ions	ammonium (NH_4^+) ions nitrate (NO_3^-) ions amino acids peptides nucleotides proteins (some basidiomycota)
Mineral salts (Macronutrients)	phosphorus potassium magnesium iron sulphur calcium chlorine (algae)	phosphorus potassium magnesium iron sulphur calcium sodium (bacteria)
(Micronutrients)	boron cobalt manganese copper zinc molybdenum (cyanobacteria) vanadium (cyanobacteria)	boron cobalt manganese copper zinc molybdenum (bacteria) vanadium (bacteria)
Growth factors		some vitamins of B–complex (required as co-enzymes)

(a) In liquid (broth) media

Unit samples are withdrawn at regular intervals. Biomass of the micro-organism, after filtration and drying, is recorded.

(b) On solid media

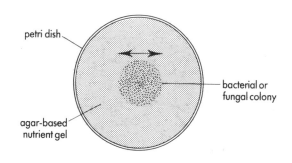

Successive measurements of the bacterial or fungal colony are made, as it spreads from a central point on the agar plate.

Figure 18 Two methods for determining the growth rates of micro-organisms

in liquid media. At the centre of the haemocytometer are one or more grids, overlaid by a specially designed coverglass. Viewed under the high-power of a microscope, an observer sees a central unit of 25 squares (Figure 19b). Each of these 25-squared units usually measures $0.2 \times 0.2 \times 0.1$ mm (depth) and has a volume of 0.004 mm^3. After making a count of the number of cells in one of these units, the observer multiplies the figure by 250 000 to give the approximate number of cells in 1 cm^3 of the cell suspension. Thus in Figure 19b, a total count of the 40 cells would give an estimate of $40 \times 250\ 000 = 10\ 000\ 000$.

Counts of living cells can be made by progressive or **serial dilutions**, carried out as follows. Ten tubes which each contain 9 cm^3 of distilled water, are set up in a rack. A sterile

pipette is used to place 1 cm^3 of the original cell suspension in tube 1. After shaking, 1 cm^3 of this suspension is then added to tube 2, and so on. Ten nutrient agar plates are then prepared and numbered. After transferring 1 cm^3 of each suspension to the corresponding plate, and spreading it with an L-shaped spreader, the plates are incubated until colonies of bacteria, yeast or algae are visible. If 41 colonies grew on plate No. 8, then

No. living cells/1 cm^3 suspension =
$41 \times 100\ 000\ 000 = 4\ 100\ 000\ 000$

A colorimeter can be used in a **photometric method** for estimating cell density during population growth. Unit samples are withdrawn at regular intervals and transferred to a test-tube. The optical density (absorbance) of the cell

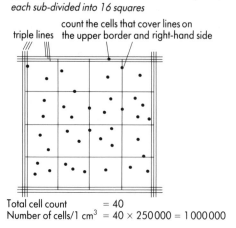

(a) A haemocytometer

coverglass   H-shaped drainage well

plastic or glass base

2nd grid   1st grid

(b) The 25 squares at the centre of each grid

sample depth = 0.1 mm

1 mm

1 mm

(c) Magnified view of one of the 25 central squares, each sub-divided into 16 squares

count the cells that cover lines on
triple lines   the upper border and right-hand side

Total cell count   = 40
Number of cells/1 cm^3 = 40 × 250000 = 1000000

Figure 19   Using a haemocytometer for total cell counts

Tube No.:	1	2	3	4	5
Dilution:	10^{-1}	10^{-2}	10^{-3}	10^{-4}	10^{-5}

1 part   1 part   1 part   1 part   1 part

Tube No.:	6	7	8	9	10
Dilution:	10^{-6}	10^{-7}	10^{-8}	10^{-9}	10^{-10}

1 part   1 part   1 part   1 part

Number of living cells
= 41 × 10^7
= 410000000

Figure 20   Dilution procedure for serial plating

suspension is measured and recorded. As cell numbers increase there is a related increase in light absorption and turbidity. A graph of optical density against time is plotted. This work can be made quantitative if the colorimeter is first calibrated with known masses of a dried micro-organism, such as yeast suspended in unit volumes of water.

2.3.1 Growth curves in liquid media

Bacteria, yeasts and populations of unicellular organisms, grown in liquid media with limited amount of nutrients, show a characteristic sigmoid growth curve, similar to the generalised curve shown in Figure 21. This curve has four basic phases:

   (i) the lag phase
   (ii) the log phase, or exponential growth phase
   (iii) the stationary phase
   (iv) the senescent phase, death phase or logarithmic decline phase.

lag phase | log phase, or exponential growth phase | stationary phase | senescent phase, or death phase

negative acceleration

Cell numbers

Time (hours or days)

Figure 21   The generalised growth curve of a cell population (real populations often fluctuate around an equilibrium level)

24

During the **lag phase**, which may last from a few minutes to several days, there is little or no increase in cell numbers. Individual cells show intense metabolic activity, notably enzyme synthesis, during this phase. Near the end of the lag phase cells may increase in size, sometimes doubling or tripling their mass and volume. Soon, in the **log phase**, or **exponential growth phase**, the cells begin to divide at a constant rate. Ideally the cell population increases geometrically, in the series 2, 4, 8, 16, 32, 64, 128 etc. This rate of increase, however, is not maintained indefinitely. In substrate-limited growth media, the growth rate slows as nutrients begin to run out. Furthermore, at this stage of their growth, many unicellular organisms produce secondary metabolites (e.g. ethanol) that have a toxic effect, slowing the rate of cell division. The combined effects of this shortage of nutrients and accumulation of toxins are that the growth rate becomes progressively slower. At a point where the birth rate of new cells is equal to the death rate of old ones, population growth enters the **stationary phase**. In this phase the population is more or less constant. It is drawn as a flat, straight line in Figure 21, but may actually be characterised by marked variations in numbers (dotted line), fluctuating on both sides of a mean. When all the food in a nutrient solution has been used up, the number of cell deaths exceeds the number of new cells produced. This marks the beginning for the **senescent phase**, or **death phase**, a period of logarithmic decline. At the end of this period only a few extremely resistant cells may remain, or the population might die out entirely.

If fungal hyphae are grown in liquid media, a flatter growth curve, without a senescent phase, is usually obtained (Figure 23). Again, there is a lag phase, followed by exponential growth, but fungal hyphae rarely grow as rapidly as unicellular organisms. Secondary metabolites, such as antibiotics, are produced towards the end of exponential growth. Mycelial mats, formed from intertwined hyphae, are removed during the stationary phase, so that the mass of the hyphae, rarely falls after exponential growth is complete.

2.3.2 Exponential Numbers

When biologists plot a growth curve to show changes in cell density, they often plot cell numbers on a logarithmic rather than an arithmetic scale. One reason for this is that actual cell numbers, which can increase in a few hours from tens to billions, are difficult to plot on standard graph paper. Another reason is that exponential growth is shown as a straight line on a logarithmic scale, whereas it would be shown as a curve on an ordinary scale. Straight line graphs

Figure 22   The generalised growth curve of fungal hyphae growing on liquid media

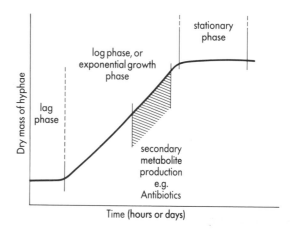

Figure 23   The generalised growth curve of a cell population plotted on a logarithmic scale

are much easier to draw and interpret accurately than curved ones.

A logarithmic scale is based on exponential numbers. The number 100, for example, can be written as 10^2. Here, 2 is its **exponent** or **logarithm to base 10**. Similarly, the logarithm of 10 (or 10^1) is 1 and of 1000 (or 10^3) is 3. Numbers between 100 and 1000 have logarithms between 2.0 and 3.0. Numbers between 10 and 100 have logarithms between 1.0 and 2.0. So an increase of one unit (or log 10) on a logarithmic scale represents a multiplication by ten on an ordinary scale. Likewise, an increase of log 2 on a logarithmic scale represents a multiplication by two on an ordinary scale. Figure 23 shows the approximate shape of the curve of Figure 21 to a logarithmic scale.

An understanding of exponential numbers is essential in the operation of industrial processes involving the growth of micro-organisms. In such processes, operators need to predict approximate times for cultures to reach required levels of cell density.

During the log or exponential growth phase shown in Figures 21 and 23, the cells are dividing at a constant rate. Cell numbers will double in a unit period of time, known as the **mean generation time**. Each species has its own mean generation time, which is genetically determined. If we know the mean generation time in minutes, t, we can calculate the number of generations per hour, k, by using the equation

$$k = \frac{60}{t} \qquad (1)$$

The name given to k is the **exponential growth rate constant**, and it, too, varies from species to species. A species with a mean generation time of 20 minutes would have an exponential growth rate constant of 3. An initial population of 500 individuals of this species would have increased to 1000 (500 x 2) after 20 minutes, to 2000 (500 x 2^2) after 40 minutes, and to 4000 (500 x 2^3) after one hour. If we call the initial population N_o, we can therefore calculate N_{1H}, the population one hour later, using the equation

$$N_{1H} = N_o \times 2^k$$
$$= 500 \times 2^3 = 4\,000$$

(note that k will not always be a whole number)

If we want to calculate the population after some other length of time we need a more general equation. If T is the time in hours between the first and second measurements, we can use

$$N_T = N_o \times 2^{Tk} \qquad (2)$$

Alternatively, if g is the number of generations (or mean generation times) which have occurred between the two measurements, we can use

$$N_g = N_o \times 2^g$$

Suppose now that we have a population of an unknown species, and we wish to calculate its mean generation time. We could measure the initial population density and then take a second measurement some known time later. The two measurements and the number of hours between them could be substituted in equation 2, and then k could be calculated. However k must first be made the subject of the equation:

First taking logs of both sides of equation 2:
$$\log N_T = \log N_o + Tk \log 2$$

Rearranging to make k the subject of the equation,

$$k = \frac{\log N_T - \log N_o}{T \log 2} \qquad (3)$$

The mean generation time is then found by substituting for k in equation 1.

Example 1

A certain species has an exponential growth rate of 2.5. If an initial population of 1000 individuals undergoes exponential growth for six hours what is its final population?

As we need to find N_T, the population after given time T (in hours), we use equation (2). Substituting the values we know for the initial population, the time elapsed and the exponential growth rate constant:

$$N_{(6\,hours)} = 1000 \times 2^{(6 \times 2.5)}$$
$$= 1000 \times 2^{(15)}$$
$$= 1000 \times 32\,724$$

The final population can therefore be calculated to be approximately 32.8 million individuals.

Example 2

A population of a species with an unknown exponential growth rate constant is left to grow exponentially for 2½ hours. At the beginning of the period a population of 550 individuals is measured, and at the end it is found to have grown to 16 000. Find the exponential growth rate constant for this species, and use it to calculate the mean generation time.

In this case we know the values of T, N_T and N_o, and we need to find k, so we use equation (3). Substituting the known values into the equation, we obtain

$$k = \frac{\log (16\,000) - \log (550)}{2.5 \log 2}$$

We can therefore calculate that k is approximately 1.94.

To find t, the mean generation time in minutes, we substitute for k in equation (1).

$$\text{This gives } t = \frac{60}{1.94}$$

So the mean generation time is approximately 30.9 minutes, or 30 minutes and 54 seconds.

2.4 ECOLOGY

Micro-organisms play a more important role in food chains and biogeochemical cycles than their small size might at first suggest. Cyanobacteria and algae are important **producers** in many aquatic food chains. Protozoans are **consumers**, while saprophytic bacteria and fungi are **decomposers**, breaking down dead organisms into simpler compounds that can be recycled back to the producers (Figure 24).

Each micro-organism has a minimum temperature (below which it cannot grow) an optimum temperature (at which growth is most rapid) and a maximum temperature (above which growth is not possible). Interestingly, the optimum temperature is always nearer to the maximum than the minimum (Figure 25). On the

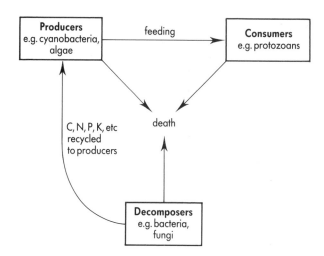

Figure 24 *The ecological roles of micro-organisms*

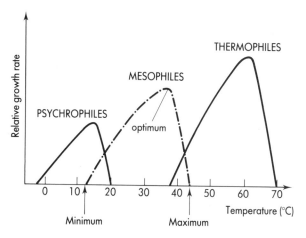

Figure 25 *Temperature limits and growth rates of psychrophiles, mesophiles and thermophiles*

basis of their optimum temperatures, it is possible to distinguish three ecologically distinct groups of micro-organisms:

(i) **Psychrophiles** (cryophiles), with low optimum temperatures, occur mainly in Arctic and Antarctic regions. Some bacteria belonging to this group may contaminate refrigerated foods, in which they can multiply at a relatively rapid rate.

(ii) **Mesophiles**, with medium optimum temperatures live in tropical and sub-tropical regions, or in warm-blooded animals.

(iii) **Thermophiles**, with high optimum temperature, live in thermal springs, or pools fed by geysers.

These three groups of micro-organisms are of great interest to biotechnologists, because their enzymes are adapted to operate most efficiently at specific temperatures close to their optima.

Just as each micro-organism has a temperature range within which growth is possible, so it also

has its own pH range, with minimum, optimum and maximum points. In general, micro-organisms are better adapted to acid environments than plants or animals. For instance, some green algae, including *Chlorella*, have a lower pH limit of 1–2, while some bacteria and fungi will survive below pH 0.8. Cyanobacteria, on the other hand, are never found in habitats in which the pH is less than 4.0. This means that they are one of the first groups of micro-organisms to be killed when lakes become acidified.

2.5 NITROGEN CYCLE

The nitrogen cycle is shown in Figure 26. All four stages of the nitrogen cycle: nitrogen fixation, ammonification, nitrification and denitrification depend on micro-organisms. This illustrates the importance of micro-organisms in terrestrial and aquatic environments. From a chemical viewpoint, the micro-organisms that derive the nitrogen cycle synthesise nitrogenous compounds, transform one nitrogenous compound into another, and degrade N-containing macromolecules into simpler compounds so that they can be recycled. We will look at the four processes in turn.

Nitrogen fixation

This is the reduction of nitrogen by hydrogen to form ammonia (NH_3). A wide range of free-living soil bacteria are capable of carrying out this reaction. They include aerobes such as *Azotobacter* and *Pseudomonas*, together with anaerobes such as *Clostridium*, *Chromatium* and *Chlorobium*. Bacteria of the genus *Rhizobium* are of particular interest, because they can fix nitrogen when in a symbiotic relationship with the roots of legumes.

The biochemistry of nitrogen fixation is similar in all organisms that have been studied. It depends on the enzyme nitrogenase, which has either molybdenum or vanadium as one of its components. Indeed, some bacteria such as *Azotobacter chroococcum* can make both types of nitrogenase, each with a different heavy metal. ATP is required for nitrogen fixation, which results in the simultaneous oxidation of ferredoxin, a hydrogen acceptor.

Reduced ferredoxin ⟶ Oxidised ferredoxin
$$N_2 + 3H_2 \xrightarrow[\text{ATP} \longrightarrow \text{ADP}]{\text{nitrogenase}} NH_3$$

Most legumes, grown in their natural habitats, form symbiotic associations with bacteria of the genus *Rhizobium*. In most cases each species of legume has its own nitrogen-fixing organism,

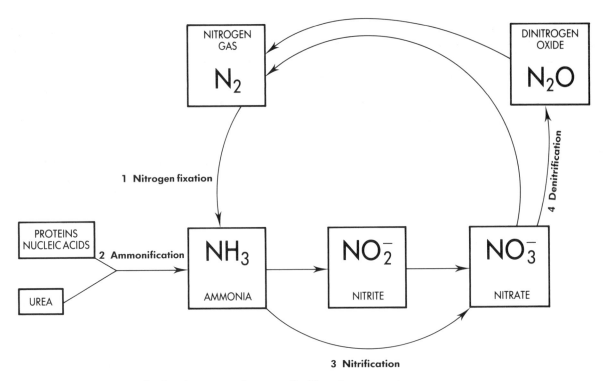

Figure 26   Four processes in the nitrogen cycle controlled by micro-organisms

present in swellings called **root nodules** that develop on the roots of infected plants. Thus *R. japonicum* occurs in soya bean, *R. trifolii* in clover and *R. meliloti* in alfalfa. Soon after entering a root hair, the rod-shaped *Rhizobium* loses its cell wall, and multiplies to form Y, X, T or J-shaped **bacteroids**, typically with dark transverse bands. The legume responds to the invasion by producing indole acetic acid (IAA) and cytokinins, growth hormones which stimulate surrounding root tissue to swell, forming a nodule. Nitrogen fixation involves the transfer of hydrogen ions from carbohydrates, such as glucose, to nitrogen. The site of transfer is the enzyme nitrogenase, located in the cytoplasm of bacteroids, in regions of the cell that are protected from oxygen. Ammonia is the initial product of the reaction, but this is soon combined with glutamate, in a reaction catalysed by glutamine synthetase, to form the amino acid glutamine.

Glutamate

$N_2 \rightarrow NH_3 \rightarrow$ Glutamine $\rightarrow$ Other amino acids $\rightarrow$ Proteins

The bacterium benefits from receiving a supply of carbon compounds from the legume, together with an anaerobic environment in which its nitrogenase can function. This environment is provided largely by the presence of a red pigment, **leghaemoglobin**, that surrounds the bacteroids,

(a) *General appearance*

(b) *Sectional view*

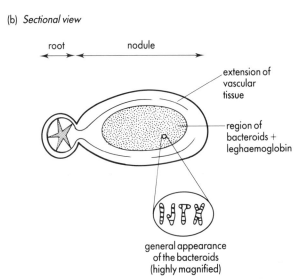

Figure 27   *Root nodules in legumes*

28

absorbing oxygen molecules from the surrounding soil in a manner similar to the binding between animal haemoglobin and oxygen. The legume, of course, benefits by receiving a supply of NH_3 from the bacterium, without being dependent on a supply of ammonium or nitrate ions from the soil. This means that legumes can survive and produce crops in nitrogen-deficient soils, unable to support other crop plants.

The ability of symbiotic *Rhizobium* bacteria to fix atmospheric nitrogen as ammonia, and make it available to legumes, is a biological feature that genetic engineers would like to transfer to other crop plants, notably cereals. Such a transfer would greatly reduce the need for nitrogenous fertilisers, and help solve the problem of water pollution by nitrates. Nitrogenases, the enzyme systems responsible for nitrogen fixation, have two components. One of these, 'dinitrogenase', binds N_2. The other 'dinitrogenase reductase' converts N_2 to NH_3. Genes which code for these nitrogenase proteins are called *nif*-genes. Between 17–21 *nif*-genes are believed to code for the molybdenum-containing Mo-nitrogenase. A different set of *nif*-genes codes for the vanadium-containing V-nitrogenase. It appears that by having both enzyme systems, the bacterium can fix nitrogen over a wide range of temperature, V-nitrogenase being more efficient when the weather is cold. The complexity of *nif*-genes, both in their numbers and the fact that they may occur scattered throughout the genome, presents difficult problems for the genetic engineers who are working to transfer the capacity for nitrogen fixation to other crop plants with a 'built in' capacity for nitrogen fixation.

Certain cyanobacteria also fix nitrogen. *Anabaena* (see section 1.3) is a free-living genus, abundant in rice paddies and other shallow areas in tropical and temperate wetlands. Biologists are currently searching for strains which fix N_2 in excess of the bacterium's own requirements, and which release excess nitrogen as ammonia. *Nostoc*, another nitrogen-fixer, forms symbiotic associations with a small number of eukaryotic species. In lichens, where it associates with ascomycete fungi, *Nostoc* synthesises photosynthetic products and ammonia, which can pass to its fungal partner. The fungus, in return, provides *Nostoc* with a moist, shaded, well aerated habitat, together with a supply of water and mineral salts. Liverworts of the genus *Anthoceros* have gall-like structures on the underside of their thalli. The presence of *Nostoc* in these swellings makes the liverworts greener in appearance, more metabolically active, and faster-growing. Certain cycads carry colonies of *Nostoc* in their coralloid roots. These specialised respiratory roots, formed at the soil surface, receive just enough light for photosynthesis and

nitrogen fixation. Again, the cycads probably gain ammonia from their association with *Nostoc*. So does one angiosperm, the so-called giant rhubarb, belonging to the genus *Gunnera*. The enormous leaves of this plant, originating at ground level from a short rhizome, carry colonies of *Nostoc* intracellularly in cells at the base of their petioles.

Ammonification
This is the process by which proteins, amino acids, nucleic acids and nucleotides from dead organisms, together with urea from living animals, undergo degradation to form ammonia. Aerobic bacteria and fungi are among the many heterotrophic soil micro-organisms that hydrolyse N-containing molecules, liberating NH_3 as an end product.

Nitrification
This is the oxidation of ammonia to nitrite (NO_2^-) and nitrate (NO_3^-) and is achieved by two different genera of soil bacteria, *Nitrosomonas* and *Nitrobacter*.

Nitrosomonas, an obligate aerobe, converts ammonia to nitrite, in the overall reaction:
$$2NH_3 + 3O_2 \rightarrow 2HNO_2 + 2H_2O$$
Nitrobacter, another obligate aerobe, completes the oxidation by converting nitrite to nitrate:
$$2HNO_2 + O_2 \rightarrow 2HNO_3$$
Green plants are able to take up and assimilate the nitrate that this bacterium produces.

Denitrification
This is the reduction of nitrate in the soil to oxides of nitrogen and nitrogen gas and has a detrimental effect on soil fertility. It occurs chiefly in waterlogged soils, with a high organic content, and is caused largely by the anaerobic bacterium *Pseudomonas dentrificans*, and some species of *Thiobacillus*.

The stages in the reduction of nitrate are as follows:

NO_3^-	$\rightarrow$	NO_2^-	$\rightarrow$	N_2O	$\rightarrow$	N_2
Nitrate		Nitrite		Dinitrogen oxide (Nitrous oxide)		Nitrogen

2.6 HUMAN PATHOGENS

A number of micro-organisms cause human diseases. These are called **human pathogens**. In response to large, active molecules, **antigens**, on the surface of these pathogens, humans produce protective proteins called **antibodies**. Each antibody is antigen-specific, and gives protection against further attack by that antigen. The principal of the protective procedure known as vaccination is to induce antibody protection, without causing symptoms or disease, and so to make the vaccinated person immune. **Vaccines** are made from killed, inactivated or genetically modified micro-organisms, or their active products. One major aim of biotechnology is to increase the range of vaccines available and to improve their effectiveness.

Mumps

Mumps is an acute contagious disease caused by an enveloped helical virus fragmented single-stranded RNA. After entering the respiratory tract it multiplies in the mouth and oropharynx. About 16–21 days after exposure to the virus the first symptoms appear. One or both parotid glands – the salivary glands located just below and in front of the ear – swell up and become painful. Virus particles appear in the saliva, then several days later in the urine. Complications may include inflammation of the testes or ovaries, in those who have reached puberty, or the pancreas and the membranes surrounding the brain. The disease is transmitted in droplets of fluid that originate in the oropharynx, and are expelled during breathing, speaking, coughing and sneezing. Transmission of the virus is helped by moist, warm conditions, and close contact with infected persons. Full recovery may take 2 – 3 weeks. A vaccine, measles-mumps-rubella (MMR), is available.

AIDS

Acquired immune deficiency syndrome (AIDS) is caused by **human immunodeficiency virus (HIV)**. This is a **retrovirus**, one that synthesises DNA using its RNA as a template. All carriers of the disease have virus particles in various cells, notably in T-helper lymphocytes and cells of their nervous system. As the disease progresses, viruses also appear in the blood, saliva and tears, together with semen in men and vaginal secretions in women. On entering a cell, the virus may behave in any one of three different ways:

(i) It may integrate a DNA copy of its genome into the host cell chromosome. Viral DNA is then replicated as a chromosomal gene, without any obvious ill effects on the host cell.

(ii) From the DNA copy of its genome on the host cell chromosome, it may transcribe a few molecules of viral RNA. These become surrounded by part of the host cell membrane to form complete viruses. This process may damage the host cell, but rarely kills it.

(iii) Again, from its DNA copy on the host cell chromosome, the virus transcribes large numbers of viral RNA molecules, together with the kinds of mRNA needed to make viral coats, which are the protein coverings of a virus. Many viruses are produced in

this process. The cell dies when it bursts to release viruses into the body fluids.

HIV is transmitted principally by contact during heterosexual or homosexual intercourse. It may also be passed from person to person during blood transfusions with contaminated blood, or via dirty hypodermic needles.

The disease has an unusually long incubation period. It can be up to nine years before those who are infected with the virus develop 'full blown' AIDS. Symptoms such as fever, weight loss, diarrhoea, night sweats and persistent cough develop. Progressive destruction of the T-helper lymphocytes affects all the other cell types in the immune system. This is because the T-helper lymphocytes play a central role in co-ordinating other cells of the immune system, by secreting activating substances called **lymphokines**. The consequences of the failure of this activation, are as follows:

(i) Phagocytes, notably neutrophils and monocytes, which normally ingest viruses cannot remove them from the body fluids.

(ii) B-lymphocytes, responsible for producing antibodies, do not reproduce themselves in response to antigens. As a result a

Human immunodeficiency virus (HIV), the causative agent of AIDS

Kaposi's sarcoma

B-lymphocyte cannot make enough of its antibody to neutralise the complementary antigen.

(iii) T-killer cells, which seek out and destroy any foreign cells, including those responsible for causing cancer, become less efficient.

As the disease progresses there is an added complication, because any cells infected with HIV may become a target for T-killer cells. Hence, the immune system often becomes self-destructive. Furthermore, tissues may also be destroyed because HIV randomly 'switches on' clones of antibody-producing B-cells. Some of these antibodies attack the host's own tissues, causing muscle wastage and general loss in body mass. 'Opportunist' infections may set in. One of the most common is *Pneumocystis carnii*, an otherwise rare form of pneumonia. An equally rare form of cancer, Kaposi's sarcoma, also occurs in AIDS sufferers. Such conditions are found only in people who have had their immune systems severely damaged.

At the end of 1988 more than six million people worldwide were believed to be infected with HIV. In the UK alone there were more than 50 000 carriers; more than 2000 people had 'full-blown' AIDS, and there had been 1059 deaths since records began. At present, there is no cure for AIDS. Only preventative measures are available. These include screening all blood samples for HIV antibodies before using them in blood transfusions. Sexually active people are urged to remain with one partner. Men who have more than one sexual partner are advised to wear condoms. For those who are infected, a drug known as zidovudine, formerly called AZT, slows the progress of the disease by inhibiting the enzyme reverse transcriptase, used by the virus to make DNA from RNA (Figure 29).

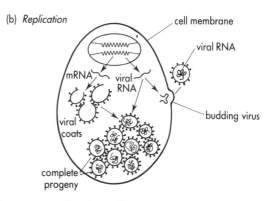

Figure 29   Behaviour of HIV, a retrovirus, in a host cell. The virus may remain integrated in the host cell's nucleus, bud off progeny from its cell membrane or form many progeny in its cytoplasm

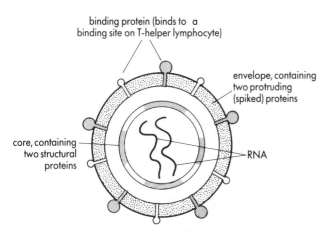

Figure 28   Cross-sectional view of a human immunodeficiency virus (HIV), the cause of AIDS. An outer coat with binding proteins, and two layers of structural proteins, surround two strands of RNA

Figure 30   The central role of T-helper lymphocytes in the human immune system. Activation is by means of hormone-like compounds called lymphokines

31

In the future it may be possible to produce an effective vaccine. Spike proteins on the surface of the virus mutate very frequently, but other proteins in the viral coat, known as CD4-recognising proteins, are more stable. By blocking these sites, so that they cannot bind CD4-proteins on the surface of T-helper cells, it may be possible to protect these cells from attack.

Salmonellosis

Salmonellosis, otherwise known as 'food poisoning' or gastroenteritis, is an acute intestinal infection caused by bacteria of the genus *Salmonella*. It is important to realise that there are many different species of *Salmonella*. For example, *S. typhii* causes typhoid fever, a virulent intestinal disease that may cause the small intestine to perforate. In untreated cases the death rate may be as high as 10 per cent. Uncooked meat, together with unpasteurised milk and cheese made from it, may contain *S. typhinurium*. Chickens and eggs are a source of *S. enteriditis*. It is the disease caused by the last two organisms that is normally called salmonellosis. The symptoms, such as fever, diarrhoea and vomiting occur after swallowing a very large dose of about 100 million bacteria. These bacteria invade cells lining the small intestine. Typically, recovery takes from 1–3 days, but infants and elderly people may die, following invasion from the intestine into the blood stream. Those who recover continue to shed the organism in their faeces for up to six months.

Salmonella *bacteria*

During the late 1980s there was a particular concern about infections caused by *S. enteriditis*. This bacterium lives in the intestine of chickens and turkeys without causing any obvious ill effects. Intensive methods of poultry farming, in which large numbers of birds are kept together in batteries or deep-litter houses, provided ideal conditions for the bacterium to spread. Furthermore, the practice of processing the heads, legs, feathers and guts of slaughtered chickens, so that they could be added to chicken meal as an additional source of protein, compounded the problem. Inadequate sterilisation often failed to kill off bacteria in slaughtered birds, which meant that some of the food fed to laying birds had been contaminated at source. After slaughter, contamination from the gut and soiled skin frequently transferred infection from one carcass to another. Between 26 and 65% of all carcasses were believed to be infected.

Although thorough cooking destroyed the bacterium making the meat safe to eat, birds that had been deep frozen were often inadequately cooked. When cooking these birds complete pre-thawing is essential, otherwise meat at the centre of the bird may not reach the temperature of 68°C (145°F), which is required to kill off the bacteria.

In 1989 the incidence of salmonellosis reached epidemic proportions. The major source of infection was believed to be eggs, especially uncooked eggs or lightly cooked eggs, used for making marzipan, cake icing, mayonnaise and some alcoholic drinks. Interestingly, the bacterium had spread from the gut of some birds, where it was a fairly harmless parasite, into other tissues, where it became a symbiont. This change in its location, again without any obvious ill effects on the birds, enabled the bacterium to pass directly from parent birds to their chicks via eggs. For the consumer it now means that only hard-boiled eggs, in which all the proteins have been denatured, can be guaranteed free from infection.

Government policy has been to advise consumers about egg consumption, test eggs for *Salmonella*, slaughter infected flocks, and pay compensation to farmers. In the future a solution may lie with a vaccine, a drug or a completely effective method of sterilisation.

Malaria

Malaria is caused by a parasitic protozoan (*Plasmodium*), transmitted from one person to another by an insect carrier, the female anopheline mosquito. Once quite common in low-lying parts of the UK, the disease occurs today in tropical Asia, Africa and in Central and South America. Sufferers experience periodic chills and fever, with vomiting and severe headache. A bite from an infected mosquito injects a form of the parasite called a **sporozoite** into the bloodstream.

On arrival at the liver the sporozoite enters liver cells and multiplies to form cysts. When a cyst bursts it releases thousands of spherical spores, called **merozoites**, into the bloodstream. Others, however, remain in the liver, forming a reservoir from which they emerge months or even years later to cause a recurrence of the disease. The role of each merozoite is to enter a red blood cell where it grows to form an amoeboid stage called a **trophozoite**.

Rapid growth of the trophozoite is followed by its division into 8, 16 or 32 more merozoites, depending on the species. Release of these merozoites, normally at 1–3 day intervals, is accompanied by an intensification of the symptoms. In addition to the recurrent symptoms, the long-term effects of malaria include anaemia through loss of red blood cells. There may also be degenerative changes in the liver and spleen.

The parasite's life cycle continues when a mosquito bites an infected person and sucks up blood containing merozoites that have matured into **gametocytes**. From these, small male and larger female gametes develop as soon as the blood meal reaches the mosquito's stomach. Here, the male gamete divides to form eight **sperms**. Fusion between a sperm and female gamete produces a motile **zygote**, which bores outwards through the stomach wall. On the outside of the stomach the zygote grows into an **oocyst** in which thousands of sporozoites form. When the oocyst burst, and the sporozoites pass via the blood into the salivary glands, the life cycle is complete. Note that the mosquito is not merely a passive carrier of the micro-organism; rather, it acts as a secondary host. Reproduction of the parasite inside its vector increases the number of individuals that can infect a new host. The mosquito therefore brings about an active or **biological transmission**.

Malaria is one of the commonest of the tropical diseases. Before specific control measures were introduced there were about 250 million cases worldwide, with an annual death rate toll of around 2.5 million. Malaria control is directed either against the malarial parasite in its human host, or against the mosquito that transmits the disease. Drugs such as amodiaquine, chloroquine, proguaril, primaquine and pyrimethanine have been used since the late 1950s. In that time some strains of *P. falciparum* have become resistant to chloroquine, a drug that prevents the merozoite stage from replicating by fitting between base pairs in the DNA. More recent drugs include fansidar, maloprim and mefloquine, but again there is some evidence that resistant strains are emerging.

A better long-term solution appears to lie with vaccines. A two step approach has been adopted. Firstly, antigens on the surface of the parasite's four stages (sporozoite, trophozoite, nerozoite and gametocyte) have been identified. Next, the genes that code for these proteins have been used to transform bacteria (p. 00), so that they secrete the proteins in large amounts. From these specific antigens, against which the human immune system reacts, it is hoped to produce an effective vaccine against the disease.

The second line of attack, against the *Anopheles* mosquito, has taken many forms. Wetlands were drained to destroy the insect's breeding grounds. Insecticides, including DDT and pyrethrum, were sprayed on the walls of houses. People slept in mosquito nets at night, to avoid being bitten. *Gambusia affinis*, a fish that feeds on mosquito larvae, was introduced into ponds. Numerous other predators and parasites of mosquito larvae were also used in mosquito-ridden waters. These have included viruses, the bacterium *Bacillus thuringiensis* (p.96), protozoans, fungi and a nematode worm. Surfactants and oils, sprayed over the water surface, have been used to suffocate the larvae. Chitin inhibitors and juvenile hormones,

Female anopheles mosquito (Anopheles albimanus) *feeding on human blood*

A red blood cell parasitised by two of the malaria parasite (Plasmodium falciparum)

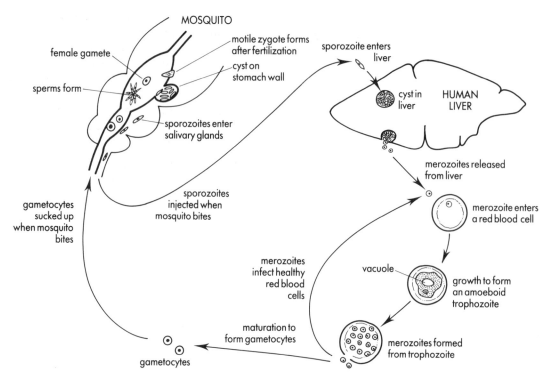

Figure 31 *The life-cycle of the malarial parasite (Plasmodium). Three stages (merozoite, trophozoite and gametocyte) are formed in the human host, and two stages are formed in the mosquito (gametes, sporozoites)*

dissolved in the water, have been utilised in an attempt to prevent the larvae from metamorphosing. Despite this onslaught against the parasite and its vector, malaria remains a widespread and common tropical disease. Containment and control appear to be more realistic aims than eradication.

Candidiasis

Candida albicans is a yeast-like fungus which often lives in a harmless 'commensal' partnership with humans. It occurs chiefly in the mouth, intestines and vagina. Although 20–30 per cent of healthy persons pass the organism in their faeces, it can also cause acute or sub-acute infections known as **candidiasis**, if it enters the bloodstream via broken skin. Infections of the mouth, commonly known as 'oral thrush', are especially common in infants. Mucous membranes lining the tongue, palate and throat become red and raw, spotted with white patches. Similar infections in adults may follow diabetes, leukaemia, alcoholism or friction from badly-fitted false teeth. 'Vaginal thrush' occurs most commonly in pregnancy and in persons suffering from diabetes, when there is glucose in the urine. Transmission from person to person may occur during intercourse. It is also quite common for *Candida* infections to follow a course of treatment with antibiotics. The antibiotic kills off the normal commensal bacteria, allowing *Candida* to take over.

Iodine-based preparations are used to treat infections that have not spread beyond the mucous membranes.

QUESTIONS

1 Using dried yeast, you prepare 100 cm³ of a 10% $^{w/v}$ suspension of yeast cells.
   a) What volume of water would you add to produce a 0.5% $^{w/v}$ suspension? Show how you arrived at your answer.
   b) The petri dish shown below was 'seeded' with 0.1 cm³ of the 0.5% $^{w/v}$ suspension. How many cells did it contain?

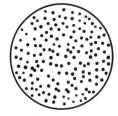

   c) From your answer in (b), estimate the number of yeast cells in 10 g dried yeast. Again, show how you arrived at your answer.

2 The graph below is a log-linear plot of the number of cells in 1 cm³ of a cell suspension.

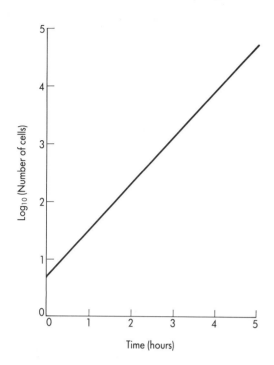

Time (hours)

a) Which part of the normal growth curve is represented by the graph?
b) What were the actual numbers of cells in the culture at (i) zero time, (ii) after 1 hour, (iii) after 2 hours and (iv) after 4 hours?
c) Give a definition of the term 'mean generation time'.
d) Use the formula $\log N_t = \log N_o + Tk \log 2$, and the actual numbers of cells in the culture after (i) 1 hour and (ii) 2 hours, to calculate the mean generation time (t) of the cell population.
e) What do you understand by the term 'exponential growth rate constant (k)'?
f) Calculate the exponential growth rate constant (k) from the value of t you have obtained in part (d).
g) Use the formula, and value of k, to predict the size of the population after 8 hours.

3 AIDS is caused by a virus which severely damages the human immune system.
a) What is the full name of the disease for which AIDS is an abbreviation?
b) Name the virus that causes AIDS.
c) List all the routes by which the disease may be transmitted from one person to another.
d) By the end of 1986 the disease affected mostly men in America, but both men and women in Africa. How would you account for this?
e) Outline the principal ways in which AIDS affects the human immune system.

f) What secondary diseases are commonly seen in AIDS sufferers whose immune systems have been severely damaged?
g) Explain the problem biologists have experienced in attempting to find a vaccine against the AIDS virus.
h) Until a cure can be found, what preventative measures should be adopted to reduce the spread of the disease?

4 The diagram below illustrates some of the stages in the nitrogen cycle.

A →
B →
C →
D →

A   B   C   D

Living animals
Legumes

N_2 NH_4^+ NO_3^-

a) Name the processes A-D.
b) Which of these processes are carried out by bacteria?
c) In what form does nitrogen occur in a legume?
d) Describe the special features of legumes that enable them to carry out process A.
e) When a legume dies, describe the processes that precede stage C. What organisms are responsible for these processes?

5 A population of cells, growing in a liquid medium in which nutrients are limited produces a characteristic growth curve.
a) Draw a diagram to show principal phases in this growth curve, and briefly explain what is happening to the cells in each phase.
b) What is a logarithmic scale?
c) Explain the advantages of plotting changes in cell density on a logarithmic scale.

6 Give a full account of two different methods you could use to measure changes in cell density in a population of bacterial or yeast cells, growing in a liquid, nutrient-limited medium.
Which method produces the most accurate data? Give one or more reasons in support of your view.

7 How do bacteria differ with regard to their
a) nutrition and
b) respiration?
Explain how the various differences you describe have been exploited by biotechnologists.

8 What is a pathogen?

Write a full account of one human pathogen that is a virus, bacterium or fungus. What precautions should be taken to prevent the pathogen you have described from spreading?

9 Describe the life-cycle of the malarial parasite (*Plasmodium*).

How does an intimate knowledge of the life cycle of this parasite enable biologists to take effective measures against (i) the parasite and (ii) its insect vector?

BIBLIOGRAPHY

Micro-organisms in action

Brock, T D (1979) *Biology of Microorganisms* 3rd Edn Prentice/Hall International, New Jersey

Garbutt, J W and Bartlett, A J (1972) *Experimental Biology with Microorganisms* Butterworths, London

Jennings, D H and Lee, D L eds (1975) *Symbiosis* Cambridge University Press

Postgate, J R (1978) *Nitrogen Fixation* (Studies in Biology No. 92) Edward Arnold

Williams, J and Shaw, M (1976) *Micro-organisms* Mills and Boon.

3 GENE EXPRESSION AND MANIPULATION

Humans share the earth with some 3–4 million other kinds of living organisms. All, from the smallest micro-organism to the blue whale, are alike in that the information determining their characteristics is encoded in long molecules of nucleic acids, either **deoxyribonucleic acid (DNA)** or **ribonucleic acid (RNA)**. Most organisms use DNA as their information-carrying genetic material, but certain viruses, such as the mumps virus, use RNA. Along the length of these nucleic acids are short active segments called **genes**. The genes act as a code for all the proteins in the body of an organism. The proteins are assembled from amino acids that are linked into chains, forming protein subunits called polypeptides. As Figure 32 shows, each and every protein, regardless of its function, is a direct representation of a particular gene. Furthermore, the protein synthesising machinery in all cells is capable of interpreting a gene in terms of the protein for which it is the code.

3.1 GENES IN EUKARYOTES

DNA is a molecule that contains all the information that a cell needs to synthesise polypeptides from amino acids. Stretched out, a DNA molecule resembles a long, spiral ladder. The two side pieces, or strands, are made from a chain of nucleotides (sugar + base + phosphate), joined end to end. Rungs across the ladder are

DNA **Proteins** **Cytoplasm**

Figure 32   The relationship between genes, proteins and cell physiology

formed by pairs of nucleotide bases. There are four types of base: adenine (A), guanine (G), cytosine (C) and thymine (T). You will see from Figure 32 that adenine always pairs with thymine (A-T) and guanine with cytosine (G-C). The two strands run parallel to one another, and are twisted to give the complete molecule the form of a double helix. The variable part of a DNA molecule, which is the biological basis of the diversity of living things, is the linear sequence of bases along the molecule. This linear sequence differs quite markedly between species, and to a smaller extent between individuals of a species. A **gene** is a length of DNA, anything from 450 to tens of thousands of base pairs in length, that acts as a code for one polypeptide.

The genetic code is arranged in triplets of bases, such as CGA, ATC, TCC etc. in both strands of the DNA molecule. Each triplet is called a **codon**. Only one strand is read for a given gene, but the opposite strand may be read for a neighbouring gene. When a cell needs to make a particular protein, part of the DNA molecule uncoils to expose a few bases of the appropriate gene. In a process known as **transcription**, an enzyme called ribonucleic acid polymerase copies one of the strands of DNA to form a molecule of **messenger RNA (mRNA)**. In this molecule the base uracil replaces thymine (Figure 34a).

Each gene on the DNA molecule consists of regions called **exons**, which are a code for part of the polypeptide. These regions are broken up by non-coding sequences called **introns**. The first mRNA transcript contains both regions. Enzymes then snip out the introns, degrade them, and splice together the remaining exons (Figure 34b). A 'cap' of several hundred bases is attached to one end of the molecule, while a 'poly-A-tail' of about 200 adenine units is attached to the other end. It is widely believed that the 'cap' is the start and the 'tail' the stop codons.

Soon after its formation the mRNA molecule leaves the nucleus and enters the cytoplasm. Here it attacts **ribosomes** and **transfer ribonucleic acid (tRNA)** molecules, while serving as a template for joining together a particular sequence of amino acids. In a process called **translation** each ribosome attaches to one end of the mRNA

(a) *Component nucleotides*

(b) *Double helix*

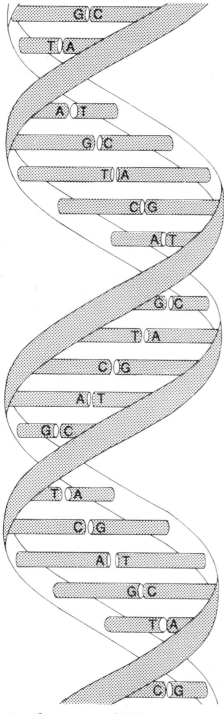

Figure 33   The structure of DNA

molecule, then moves along its length, from one end to the other. As it travels a chain of amino acids builds up. This chain, a polypeptide, is released into the cytoplasm when the ribosome has completed its run. Amino acids are brought to the ribosome by molecules of tRNA. There are several different types of tRNA, each carrying a different amino acid. Each type of tRNA has a triplet of bases, called an **anticodon**, which finds and joins up with its complementary codon on the mRNA strand. As a result amino acids are placed in an appropriate position in the polypeptide chain, and held in position by peptide bonds. After delivering its amino acid, each tRNA molecule moves away to make room for the next. The process is repeated from one end of the mRNA molecule to the other until a polypeptide has been synthesised.

Figure 34   Transcription

The genes of eukaryotes are surrounded by a collection of **signalling sequences** that are recognised by the cell. Continuous with one end of a gene is the **promoter**, a short sequence of nucleotides, to which RNA polymerase binds at the beginning of transcription. Slightly downstream of the promoter is another short nucleotide sequence, the **ribosome binding site**, where binding to a ribosome takes place. At the opposite end of a gene is the **terminator**, marking the end of the gene, where transcription stops.

(a) *Each ribosome moves along a mRNA molecule to form a polypeptide. Ribosomes may return to make further runs, depending on the needs of the cell*

(b) *Each triplet of bases (codon) on mRNA codes for one amino acid; anticodons on tRNA molecules are complimentary*

Figure 35   *Translation*

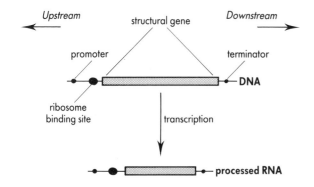

Figure 36   *Some of the signalling sequences associated with a structural gene*

3·2 GENES IN PROKARYOTES

Bacteria have a single circular chromosome. It has been estimated that this chromosome contains about 5×10^6 base pairs, has a total length of around 1 mm, and contains several thousand genes. The relationship of DNA to bacterial proteins can be represented as follows:

DNA $\xrightarrow{\text{transcription}}$ mRNA $\xrightarrow{\text{translation}}$

PROTEINS
(POLYPEPTIDES)

   When researchers began to map the distribution of bacterial genes, they were surprised to find that genes with related functions were clustered together. These clusters, now known as **operons**, regulate the rate at which certain structural genes produce proteins. For instance, the bacterium *E. coli*, an inhabitant of the human intestine, can produce lactase, an enzyme that splits lactose in milk into the monosaccharides glucose and galactose. Its access to lactose, however, depends on the amount of milk that its host drinks. Clearly, it would be wasteful for a small organism such as a bacterium to secrete lactase when it was not needed. The problem is overcome by **regulatory genes**, acting together with signalling sequences to 'switch on' or 'switch off' the structural genes for lactase production.

   The **lac operon**, illustrated in Figure 37, has three structural genes, a **regulator** gene and two signalling sequences, the **promoter** and **operator**. If there is no lactose in the bacterium's environment, the regulator gene produces a protein that binds to the operator site. When bound, this protein covers the operator and overlaps the promoter. Neither the operator nor promoter can function when blocked by the **repressor**. Under these conditions little, if any, lactase is produced. When lactose is present in excess the repressor binds to lactose molecules, thus exposing the promoter and operator sites. The enzyme RNA polymerase can then pass over the unlocked operator site and transcribe the three structural genes. This, in fact, it does by transcribing a single mRNA molecule encoding the information for all three genes, which is subsequently translated into three separate proteins.

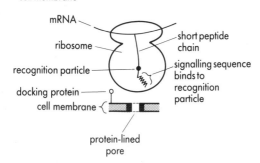

(a) When lactose is absent

(b) When lactose is present

Figure 37   Gene regulation in the lac-operon of E. coli

(a) A ribosome approaches a docking protein in the cell membrane

(b) A recognition particle binds to the docking protein; the signalling sequence binds to the membrane

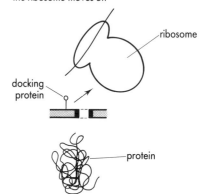

(c) Cell enzymes digest the signalling sequence. Removal of the signalling sequence allows protein synthesis

(d) Release of the protein. The membrane repairs while the ribosome moves off

Figure 38   Stages in the secretion of an extracellular protein by a bacterium

Unlike the structural genes of eukaryotes, bacterial genes do not have exons and introns. Instead, they produce mRNA transcripts that go into action as soon as they are produced, without the need for secondary processing (see Figure 34). Furthermore, although bacterial genes are associated with signalling sequences, these are different from those found in eukaryotes. All this means that if a eukaryotic gene, along with its signalling sequences, is transferred to a prokaryote, no eukaryotic proteins will normally be produced. Firstly, the bacterium does not possess the cellular machinery required to remove the introns and splice the exons. Secondly, it cannot bind or read the eukaryotic signalling sequences. These are problems that have to be overcome before prokaryotes can function as recipients of human, or other eukaryotic genes. Bacteria do, however, possess one important feature that relatively few eukaryotic cells possess, namely the ability to secrete proteins into their external medium. Figure 38 shows possible

Ribosomes and polyribosomes in the cytoplasm of a cell

stages in a process that is still not well understood. The ability of any cell to secrete proteins into its surroundings greatly simplifies the process of harvesting gene products, which can be collected from the external medium without killing off the cells that produced them.

𝟯.𝟯 GENETIC ENGINEERING

All cellular organisms contain the two nucleic acids DNA and RNA, which together make up their genetic material. Any deliberate manipulation of this material, that changes the natural sequence of nucleotides in nucleic acids, is called **genetic engineering** or **recombinant DNA technology**. More specifically, the technique may involve the addition, modification or deletion of one or more genes in a cell. To date, most genetic engineering has consisted of putting one or more extra genes into cells, so that they acquire an additional property, such as the ability to make a new protein. A successful gene transfer, from a donor organism to a recipient cell, takes place in four main steps, as follows:

(i) Removal of DNA from the donor organism, and its fragmentation to extract a particular gene or genes. Alternatively, the enzyme reverse transcriptase may be used to make DNA copies of mRNA molecules.

(ii) Incorporation of the desired gene into a vector, such as a bacteriophage or plasmid, which carries it into the recipient cell.

(iii) Incorporation of the new gene into the recipient cell's genome. (Cells of the bacterium *E. coli* and yeast (*S. cerevisiae*) are widely used as recipients by biotechnologists.)

(iv) Asexual reproduction of the recipient cells that have been transformed by incorporating the foreign gene. This important stage is called cloning. A **clone** is an entity, whether it be a bacterial cell, eukaryotic cell or gene, that is exactly alike another.

3.3.1 Extraction and preparation of genes

Cells containing the desired gene may be identified by testing for the protein that the gene makes. Any cell making this protein must have the desired gene clone. To extract the desired gene, cells may be broken down by either of two methods:

(i) Disruption by ultrasound.
(ii) Digestion in a solution of lysozyme, an enzyme that breaks down cell walls.

Disrupted cells are centrifuged to remove insoluble debris. Phenol is added to remove proteins. The slow addition of an ethanolic solution of sodium acetate precipitates strands of nucleic acid at the water-ethanol interface. These strands may be removed by winding them onto a sterile glass rod by slow rotation. After extraction the DNA is dissolved in dilute saline-citrate solution and purified by reprecipitation with ethanol. At the end of this process the operator obtains purified, crude DNA, probably containing numerous copies of each gene.

Gene selection begins when purified DNA is cut into shorter segments by adding enzymes called **restriction endonucleases**. Around 500 of these enzymes, extracted from bacteria, have been identified and made available to genetic engineers. Each one cuts DNA at specific recognition sites, consisting of anything from 2–6 paired nucleotide sequences. Cuts are either vertical, known as **blunt ends**, or staggered, known as **sticky ends**. The generation of sticky ends is particularly useful because fragments with complementary sticky ends readily join together to form larger molecules.

The material that results from DNA fragmentation may contain the whole genome of an organism, or **genomic library**. From this library a genetic engineer can select a desired gene. Figure 39 shows the method most commonly used. Firstly, gel electrophoresis is used to separate the various DNA fragments, all of different lengths, into horizontal bands, each band containing fragments of approximately the same length. (Since small fragments travel through the gel faster than large ones, the fragments separate according to their length.)

Next, radioactively labelled single-stranded DNA is added, with at least some of its base sequence complementary to the base sequence of the desired gene. Binding occurs between the radiolabelled DNA, called a **probe**, and a part of the desired gene. From this binding the position of the desired gene can be located on the gel. DNA from this region is removed. After its signalling sequences have been replaced by those of the cell into which it is to be inserted, sticky ends are attached, so that it can be carried by a vector.

An alternative approach to preparing genes for incorporation into a vector consists of synthesising the desired gene from its template mRNA. The enzyme **reverse transcriptase** catalyses the production of DNA from mRNA.

Table 4 Restriction endonucleases. Each enzyme is named according to the bacterium from which it has been isolated (e.g. Eco Rl is from E. coli)

ENZYME	RECOGNITION SEQUENCE	TYPE OF CUT
Alu l	A T C｜G T A T A G｜C A T	Blunt
Hha l	A T C G｜C A T A｜G C G T	Sticky
Eco Rl	C｜A A T T T C G T T A A A｜G	Sticky
Bam Hl	C｜G A T C G G C T A G｜C	Sticky

mRNA　　reverse transcriptase　　cDNA
$$\xrightarrow{\hspace{4cm}}$$

Many copies of complementary or copy DNA (cDNA) may result from this reaction.

3.3.2 Vectors

Some species of bacteria are able to take up DNA molecules from the medium in which they grow. Molecules of DNA taken up in this way are mostly degraded, but some may survive and become incorporated into the bacterium's genome. A more reliable method of achieving uptake and incorporation of foreign DNA depends on the use of cloning vectors. Thousands of different vectors, mostly **bacteriophages** and **bacterial plasmids**, can be used for DNA transfer. The choice, however, depends mainly on the nature of the recipient cell into which the DNA is to be transferred. Bacteria are widely used as recipient cells because there are several bacteriophages, such as λ and M 13, and a large number of bacterial plasmids, that can be used as vectors for foreign DNA. The essential requirement for a cloning vector is that it has a means of replication in its host cell. Another consideration is the amount of space available in a vector for additional (foreign) DNA. In some bacteriophages this space is very limited, especially in M 13, where the ten viral genes are tightly packed within the capsid. Nevertheless, this bacteriophage is popular with genetic engineers, because genes cloned with this vector can be obtained in the form of single-stranded DNA.

Bacteriophages, when used as gene vectors, require elaborate preparation. After removing their DNA from its surrounding capsid, cutting it, and inserting foreign DNA, the hybrid DNA must be returned to the capsid. λ Bacteriophage infection, for example, is characterised by retention of the phage DNA molecule in the host bacterium, possibly for many thousands of cell divisions. The DNA of this phage, after circularising, becomes integrated into the

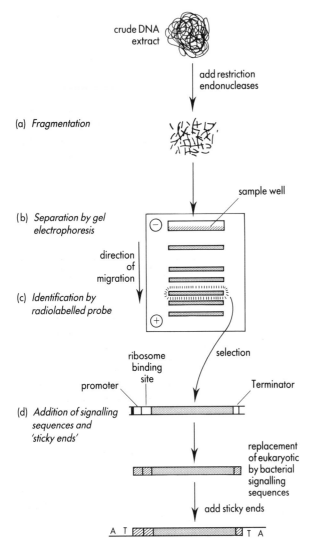

Figure 39　Stages in the preparation of an eukaryotic gene for cloning in a bacterium

(a) λ Bacteriophage

(b) M13 Bacteriophage

Figure 40   Bacteriophage gene vector

bacterial chromosome, where it remains quiescent for many generations. Eventually, however, it becomes active again, producing viral progeny. M13 bacteriophage attaches to a pileus of *E. coli* and injects its DNA. This DNA circularises and replicates in the cytoplasm of its hosts. It does not integrate with the bacterial chromosome. New phage particles are continuously assembled and released by the cell.

Plasmids are small self-replicating double-stranded circles of DNA, found in many bacteria. They carry genes that a bacterium needs only under special circumstances, such as those for antibiotic resistance, or resistance to heavy metals. The bacterium *E. coli* is the main source of plasmids used for transferring genes into bacteria.

Plasmids may be categorised in several different ways, notably as **conjugative** or **non-conjugative**, depending on whether or not they carry a set of transfer genes, called *tra*-genes, that promote bacterial conjugation. A second grouping, based on other types of genes carried by plasmids, is given in Table 5. Thirdly, plasmids that are maintained as a limited number of copies per cell are called **stringent plasmids**, whereas those that replicate freely are called **relaxed plasmids**. Genetic engineers cut plasmids with the same restriction endonucleases used to cut the donor DNA. This results in the formation of sticky ends on the plasmids that are the same as the sticky ends on the DNA segments. When mixed together the DNA segments tend to base-pair with the sticky ends of the plasmids. They are sealed together by adding **DNA-ligase**. This results in the production of a hybrid plasmid, carrying a segment of foreign DNA. It should be noted that the foreign gene usually requires both a promoter – to indicate the start of mRNA synthesis – and a terminator – to mark the end of transcription – before it will function. Once inside a bacterium, however, the plasmid becomes a functional part of the bacterium's genome. The foreign gene is expressed from its position on the plasmid, without being incorporated into the bacterial chromosome.

As many species of bacteria, including *E. coli*, will not readily take up plasmids, genetic engineers have devised treatments that improve the success rate. By soaking bacterial cells in an ice cold solution of calcium chloride ($CaCl_2$), plasmids can be made to stick to the cell walls. Their ingestion into the cytoplasm is achieved by raising the temperature to 42°C. Neither effect is fully understood.

Table 5   The five principal types of plasmid

PLASMID TYPE	GENETIC CHARACTERISTICS
R (resistance)	carry genes for resistance to one or more antibiotics and some heavy metals (e.g. mercury)
F (fertility)	carry *tra*-genes, which promote the formation of a conjugation tube, through which plasmids are transferred to other bacteria
Degradative	carry genes for the degradation of uncommon toxin such as napthalene, toluene, salicylic acid etc.
Col	carry genes which code for colicins, proteins which kill other bacteria
Virulence	carry genes which transform the host bacterium into a virulent form

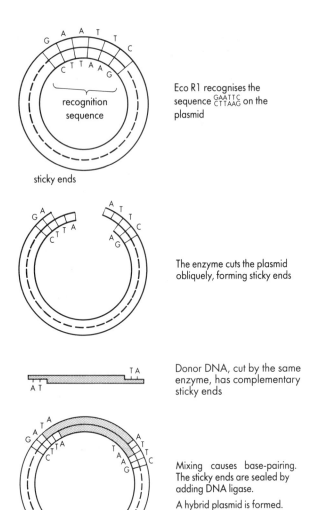

Eco R1 recognises the sequence $^{GAATTC}_{CTTAAG}$ on the plasmid

The enzyme cuts the plasmid obliquely, forming sticky ends

Donor DNA, cut by the same enzyme, has complementary sticky ends

Mixing causes base-pairing. The sticky ends are sealed by adding DNA ligase.

A hybrid plasmid is formed.

Figure 41 *Using Eco R1 to splice donor DNA into a plasmid*

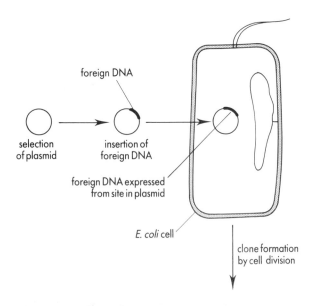

Figure 42 *Plasmid gene vectors*

Another vector of major importance in genetic engineering is the bacterium *Agrobacterium tumefaciens*, used to introduce foreign DNA into plant cells. This bacterium is a soil micro-organism, the cause of crown gall disease in many dicotyledonous species. Infected tissues swell to form tumour-like growths. The ability of the bacterium to cause this condition is associated with the presence of **Ti (tumour inducing) plasmids** within the bacterial cell. It is this plasmid that has been used as a gene vector to introduce foreign DNA into plant cells. Other cloning vectors for higher plants include the

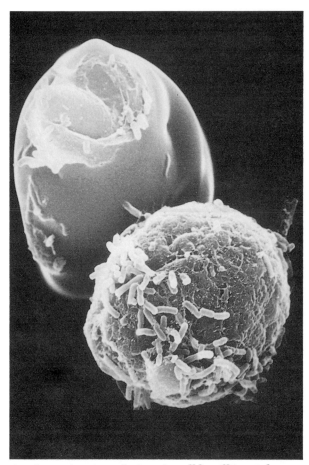

Agrobacterium tumefaciens (small bacilli) on tobacco cells

Crown gall (Agrobacterium tumefaciens) *on a loganberry bush*

cauliflower mosaic virus (CaMV), and other small plant viruses, like caulimoviruses and also geminiviruses, a recently discovered group. Simian virus 40 (SV40) and bovine papilloma virus (BPV) have been used to introduce foreign DNA into mammalian cells. BPV is of particular interest because it acts as a **shuttle vector**, with the ability to replicate its plasmids in both bacterial and mammalian cells. It can also be used to introduce quite large pieces of DNA into mammalian cells.

3.3.3 Recipients for foreign DNA

The bacterium *E. coli* and the yeast *S. cerevisiae* are widely used as recipients for foreign DNA. These unicellular, quick-growing micro-organisms are ideal for the large-scale production of bulk proteins, such as industrial enzymes, for which the economics of production are critical. Extensive studies of *E. coli* have provided a lot of information about this organism. For instance, it has several bacteriophages, and different types of plasmid, that can be used to introduce foreign DNA. Furthermore, foreign DNA introduced via a plasmid can account for up to 60 per cent of its total protein production. This bacterium, on the other hand, occurs naturally in the intestines of humans and, under certain circumstances, can cause disease.

Yeast is rarely a human pathogen. Although it is a unicellular organism, it is also a eukaryotic cell, in which the genes are organised, expressed and controlled in ways that are similar to human genes. Another advantage of yeast over *E. coli* is that it can add sugar side-chains to proteins, a common feature of some human proteins. Yeast, like *E. coli*, is very amenable to genetic engineering. Some strains of yeast have naturally occurring plasmids. Vectors derived from these are called **yeast episomal plasmids**. The word 'episomal' means that the plasmids can replicate independently, or become integrated into one of the yeast chromosomes. Moreover, some are capable of acting as shuttle vectors, replicating both in yeast and *E. coli*.

3.3.4 Transformation and cloning

From a population of 1000 or more treated cells, only one or two may take up foreign DNA and become **transformed**. Finding out which bacteria have taken up a plasmid containing foreign DNA is a two-stage process (Figure 43). *E. coli* cells treated with $CaCl_2$ are incubated with plasmids that, in addition to foreign DNA, carry genes for resistance to two antibiotics, ampicillin and tetracycline. Note that the foreign DNA is inserted into the middle of the gene for tetracycline resistance.

(i) After incubation, cells are spread out on a plate of nutrient agar containing ampicillin. Only those cells which have taken up plasmids grow on this medium. After 2–3 days the colonies of these cells are harvested. (All of the cells in these colonies will have taken up the plasmid, but not all will contain the foreign gene in active form.)

(ii) Harvested cells are then spread out on a plate of nutrient agar to which enough tetracycline has been added to prevent growth of the cells, but not to kill them. The cells that fail to grow on this medium are likely to be those that have the desired DNA segment incorporated into the gene for tetracycline resistance.

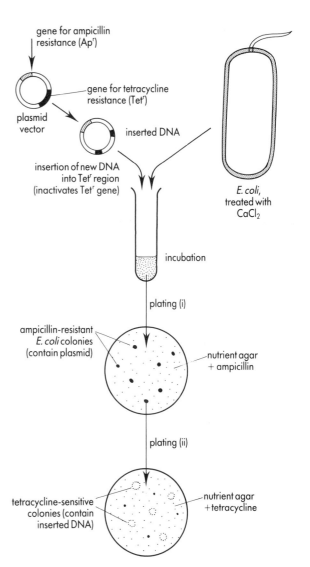

Figure 43   A common strategy for cloning DNA in E. coli

An alternative procedure identifies cells containing active foreign DNA from the protein that the new gene produces. Sometimes it is possible to apply a specific diagnostic chemical test for this protein. Another approach is to apply antibodies, coupled to dyes or radioactively labelled. As antibodies are protein-specific, and bind only to their target protein, this provides a highly specific test for cells that have acquired new functional genes.

After identification, transformed bacteria are isolated and transferred to a suitable growth medium, where they grow and multiply. This process is called gene cloning, and the genetically identical offspring are called clones. The plasmids also replicate as a bacterium multiplies, so producing many copies of any plasmid carrying foreign genes.

About 1–2 per cent of the population in the UK suffer from a deficiency of insulin, which causes diabetes mellitus. Roughly 20 per cent of these are dependent on insulin injections.

For many years the source of insulin for injection was the pancreases of slaughtered pigs and cows. Used over many years, however, these insulins proved 'immunogenic'; that is, they caused injected persons to produce antibodies against them. Human insulin was the first human hormone to be genetically engineered and produced commercially. The gene for the protein precursor of insulin, **proinsulin**, was inserted into a plasmic and cloned in *E. coli*. Following from this treatment the bacterium produced and secreted the protein proinsulin, which required further treatment before insulin was formed. This

$\mathcal{3}.4$ EXAMPLES OF PROTEIN PRODUCTION BY ENGINEERED *E. COLI*

Insulin, secreted by the pancreas, is a hormone that regulates glucose concentration in the blood.

Samples of insulin

Figure 44   Cloning genes for human insulin and growth hormone

treatment, carried out in the laboratory, involved the use of proteolytic enzymes, notably trypsin and carboxypeptidase B, to remove the so-called C chain of amino acids from the middle of the molecule, as shown in Figure 44.

Human growth hormone (HGH), secreted by the anterior pituitary gland, is needed during childhood for longitudinal growth of the skeleton. Approximately ten people per million suffer a deficiency of this hormone, leading to dwarfism. The DNA sequence that codes for this hormone was prepared in the laboratory on a DNA synthesising machine, base pair by base pair. It was then inserted into a plasmid, next to its bacterial control region. Cloned in *E. coli*, populations of transformed bacteria secreted HGH into their surroundings.

Other important proteins that can be made by genetically engineered mircro-organisms include enzymes, which have many industrial applications (see section 7.1) and adhesives, such as the protein that sticks barnacles to rock surfaces.

3.5 POSSIBLE FUTURE DEVELOPMENTS

Apart from introducing new genes into cells, there are many other genes that genetic engineers would like to block or eliminate. Cucumbers, for example, have genes that produce yellow-skinned fruits, fruits with spines (prickles), bitter-tasting fruits, and fruits that cause indigestion. Eliminating any of these genes would produce 'improved' fruits, of greater commercial value to anyone who grew them.

Humans, too, suffer from single-gene disorders, the cause of diseases such as sickle cell anaemia, cystic fibrosis and Tay-Sachs disease. Here, among biomedical researchers, the immediate aim is to map the human genome to discover the precise location of the DNA that causes these conditions. Once located, it may be possible to block the gene, so that sufferers can be offered some relief from their symptons.

At the present time effective methods of achieving these aims are still a long way off. Even so, one potentially powerful technique for blocking gene transcription is through the use of **antisense mRNA**. This is the product of a synthesised DNA molecule in which the sequence of bases, between the promoter and terminator, is the exact reverse of the 'real' gene. Introduced into a cell, and integrated into one of its chromosomes, it produces antisense mRNA (Figure 45). Contact between the two types of mRNA results in the formation of double-stranded RNA. This, in effect, locks up the 'real' mRNA molecule, so that it cannot play its normal role in translation. As a result, the polypeptide of which one of the genes is a template cannot be produced.

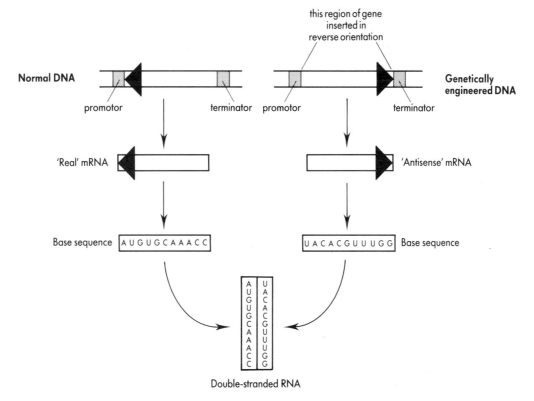

Figure 45   The use of 'antisense' mRNA to block expression of a gene

3.6 POSSIBLE SAFEGUARDS

Like many other technological advances, from the introduction of anaesthetics to the use of electricity, recombinant DNA technology could be used to harm humans as well as help them. Since the 1970s there has been public concern about the possible escape of a genetically engineered pathogen from a laboratory. Most of this concern has centred around *E. coli*, a natural inhabitant of the human intestine, which has virulent strains. The worst fears are that strains carrying plasmids with genes for human hormone synthesis, antibiotic resistance or cancer induction might escape and wreak havoc among human populations. Aware of such possibilities, however unlikely, genetic engineers have acted in the public interest by working with strains that are poorly adapted for life in the human intestine. These engineered strains may include bacteria that:

(i) grow more slowly than normal wild-type intestinal bacteria, and so would have difficulty in replacing them,
(ii) have a minimum temperature above body temperature (36°C),
(iii) contain 'suicide genes' that are activated outside certain pH or temperature limits, or
(iv) die if they lose their plasmids.

Legislation provides a further public safeguard. In the UK, guidelines for recombinant DNA work have been laid down by the Ashby Report (1975), the Godber Report (1975) and the Williams Report (1976). Work on potentially dangerous pathogens is generally restricted to isolated, purpose-built laboratories employing only highly qualified staff. Containment is achieved through strict hygienic measures, highly efficient air filters, and regular monitoring of the atmosphere within such buildings. To date, there is no evidence that genetically engineered strains of *E. coli* have been able to colonise the human alimentary canal.

Fears about the possibility that genetically engineered organisms might escape into the environment, enter food chains, and disrupt the existing balance of nature are also probably exaggerated. While it is possible that genes for herbicide resistance, say, could spread from crops to weeds, making them more difficult to kill, the effects would probably be more economic than ecological.

Humans probably have most to fear from the application of genetic engineering to biological warfare. Lethal agents that might be used in biological warfare include genetically engineered anthrax, cholera and plague bacteria. Molecular toxins, so-called because they kill or paralyse if ingested in minute quantities, can also be produced in genetically engineered bacteria and yeasts. During a war they might be released into the atmosphere or dropped into water supplies. Botulinus and tetanus toxins are extremely poisonous bacterial products that can now be made in large quantities. Other extremely toxic substances such as ricin (from castor oil seeds), saxitoxin (from fish) and tetrodoxin (from snake venom) could be made in large amounts by transferring appropriate genes to bacteria.

Influential pressure groups, with both religious and non-religious affiliations, have reservations about tinkering with the human genome. Strong opposition is likely to be expressed if genetic engineers attempt the genetic manipulation of human embryos, the addition of genes from other species to the human germ line, or fusions between human cells and those of other species. Behind such opposition is the supposition that these practices transgress the natural integrity of species, or the sanctity of the individual. On that issue, everyone has to make their own judgement.

QUESTIONS

1 Part of a DNA molecule has the following sequence:
ATCCGGTTAAGCCTAGTTACCGATTTAGCA
   a) Name the bases represented by the letters A,T,G and C.
   b) Which of these bases are pyrimidines?
   c) Write out the base sequence of a complementary mRNA molecule.
   d) On this mRNA molecule, what is a codon, and why is it so-called?
   e) How many codons are there on the mRNA molecule you have drawn?
   f) What is the base sequence of the fifth codon?
   g) If the first transcript of human mRNA contains exons and introns, how does the final transcript differ?
   h) Suppose the first mRNA molecule contained 23 per cent uracil, how much of each base would you expect the original DNA molecule to contain? Explain your answer.

2 For each of the following, construct sentences, or make annotated diagrams, to show the biological relationship of the terms listed.
   a) DNA, mRNA, thymine, uracil.
   b) DNA, mRNA, rinbonucleic acid polymerase, reverse transcriptase.
   c) Codon, anticodon, tRNA, mRNA.
   d) Ribosome, tRNA, amino acids, polypeptide chain.

e) Structural gene, promoter, operator, regulator gene.

3 The diagram below represents a plasmid before and after the insertion of a structural gene from a mammal.

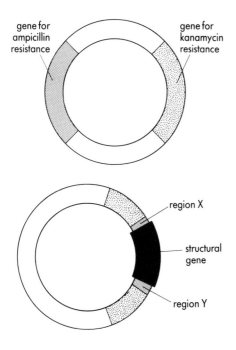

gene for ampicillin resistance

gene for kanamycin resistance

region X

structural gene

region Y

a) What type of plasmid is illustrated?
b) What is the natural function of this plasmid in bacteria such as *E. coli*?
c) Among populations of bacteria living in the wild, how is a plasmid transferred from one bacterium to another?
d) What name is given to the regions X and Y on either side of the structural gene?
e) Explain the functions of these regions.
f) Are the regions X and Y of bacterial or mammalian origin?
g) How would you find out if a bacterium, previously without plasmids, had taken up one or more of the bacterial plasmids (untransformed plasmids)?
h) Why has the mammalian structural gene been inserted in the middle of the plasmid gene for kanamycin resistance?
i) What procedure would you follow to find out if the bacterium had taken up one or more of the transformed plasmids?

4 What differences exist between
a) DNA and RNA;
b) transcription and translation;
c) exons and introns?

5 What do you understand by the terms
(i) gene vector and (ii) gene cloning?
By reference to one or more examples, describe how a genetic engineer working with plasmids and a bacterium such as *E. coli*:

a) isolates and selects a mammalian gene for cloning;
b) inserts the gene into a plasmid;
c) inserts the transformed plasmid into a bacterium;
d) detects transformed bacteria that are expressing the mammalian gene;
e) obtains a clone of transformed cells.

6 Write illustrated notes on the following:
a) Plasmids
b) Restriction endonucleases
c) Gene vectors
d) Gene cloning

7 What is genetic engineering?
Evaluate the potential advantages and disadvantages of genetic engineering.

8 Should genetic engineers attempt to manipulate the human genome? Present both sides of the argument.
Some genes, such as the gene for sickle cell anaemia, have undesirable effects. Outline possible future treatments for someone suffering from this condition. (see p.75)

BIBLIOGRAPHY

Gene expression and manipulation

Baker, JW and Allen, GE (1982) *The Study of Biology* 4th Edn. Addison Wesley

Brown, TA (1986) *Gene Cloning* van Horstrand Reinhold

Green, NPO, Stout, GW, Taylor, DJ and Soper, R (1984 and 1985) *Biological Science* (vols 1 and 2) Cambridge University Press

Kimball, J (1983) *Biology* 5th Edn. Addison Wesley

Old, RW and Primrose, SB (1985) *Principles of Gene Manipulation* 3rd Edn. Blackwell Scientific Publications

Raven, P and Johnson, G (1986) *Biology* Times Mirror Morby, St. Louis

Starr, C and Taggart, R (1987) *Biology, The Unity and Diversity of Life* 3rd Edn. Wadsworth

Villee, CA and Dethier, VG (1976) *Biological Principles and Processes* W Saunders

Villee, CA, Solomon, EP and Davis, PW (1985) *Biology* Saunders, Holt, Reinhart and Winston

Warr, JR (1984) *Genetic Engineering in Higher Organisms* Edward Arnold

Wheale, PR and McNally, RM (1988) *Genetic Engineering, Catastrophe or Utopia?* St. Martin's Press, New York

BIOTECHNOLOGY AND CHEMICAL ENGINEERING

'Biotechnology' is a relatively new name given to the use of living organisms and their products, such as enzymes, in the manufacturing or service industries. The origins of biotechnology lie deep in the mists of prehistory. From the Stone Age, about 10 000 years ago, humans have grown crops and farmed domestic animals, thereby changing their nomadic hunter-gatherer existence for one of more settled agricultural communities. Much later, without any understanding of the role of micro-organisms in the process, they baked bread, brewed beer and made cheeses from stale milk. The current revolution in biotechnology, however, owes its impact to two technological advances.

Firstly, there are the techniques of **genetic engineering**. These allow organisms to be rapidly modified, without the need for breeding, in ways that enhance their usefulness, or reduce their harmful effects. Secondly, there are the contributions of **chemical engineering**. The chemical engineers have produced machinery, including fermenters, for the large-scale production of useful cellular products, ranging from drugs to food and agricultural chemicals. The development of the **microchip** has also contributed by making biological fermentations inside large fermenters easier to monitor and control.

4.1 GOODS AND SERVICES

A major aim of biotechnology is to improve the quality of human life by providing additional goods and services. The goods, mostly in the form of consumables, include food, drugs and fuels. The services include environmental controls such as water purification and waste disposal. As Figure 46 shows, there are four production industries and one service industry, that are most likely to benefit from genetic engineering, large-scale fermentation processes, or both. These are as follows:

Production industries
(i) The manufacture of foods and drinks.
(ii) The manufacture of drugs, vaccines, diagnostics and health-care products.
(iii) Production of industrial chemicals and fuels.
(iv) Agriculture and horticulture.

Service industries
(i) Water purification and waste disposal.
The combined applications of genetic engineering and chemical engineering to biotechnology have not only led to improvements in existing manufacturing processes, but to a whole range of applications not previously thought possible. Some of these applications, currently in use or under development, are listed in Table 6.

Assembley line check on drug capsules prior to their packaging

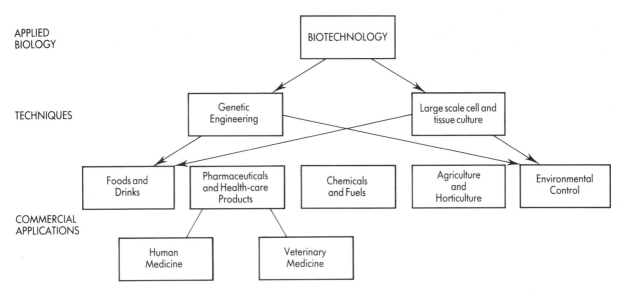

APPLIED BIOLOGY

TECHNIQUES

COMMERCIAL APPLICATIONS

Figure 46   The major techniques in contemporary biotechnology, and some of their commercial applications

Table 6   Present and potential applications of biotechnology

AREA OF APPLICATION	PRODUCT/POTENTIAL APPLICATION/AIM
Food production	bread-making; manufacture of cheese, yoghurt, butter and other dairy products; production of rennet substitutes, for cheese-making; production of vinegar; manufacture of monosodium glutamate, a flavour enhancer; extraction of 'natural' colourings from algae; production of single cell protein (SCP)
Alcoholic drinks	manufacture of beer, cider, wines and spirits
Medicines, pharmaceuticals and health-care products	production of antibiotics; synthesis of enzymes with therapeutic value; production of monoclonal antibodies; production of highly specific vaccines to induce specific antibodies in response to pathogen antigens; synthesis of human proteins (e.g. insulin, HGH) by bacteria and yeasts; synthesis of human proteins in the milk and eggs of transgenic animals; use of gene probes to identify harmful genes in human embryos; use of gene therapy to eliminate harmful single-gene traits (e.g. cystic fibrosis); 'genetic fingerprinting' for forensic and medical identification; biosensors for estimating glucose, urea, cholesterol etc. in body fluids
Chemicals	enzymes for industrial, analytical and manipulative processes; production of industrial solvents (e.g. acetone); extraction of copper, nickel and uranium from their ores; production of xanthan gum to assist oil extraction; manufacture of nerve gases and toxins for biological warfare;
Fuels	manufacture of ethanol for combustion engines; manufacture of biogas (methane)
Agriculture and horticulture	increased crop plant resistance to disease, drought, frost, herbicides and insects; better salt tolerance (e.g. rice, cereals); transfer of *nif*-genes for nitrogen fixation from legumes to cereals and other crops; introduction of genes for flavour, colour, shape etc. into fruits and vegetables; micropropagation of plants with unique combinations of genes (e.g. oil palms, house plants); increased milk, meat and egg yields in farm animals; faster growth rates in farm animals; better disease-resistance, cold-hardiness and heat-tolerance in farm animals; improved reproduction rates in farm animals by multiple births, surrogate mothering etc.; production of animal feedstocks from single cell protein;
Environmental control	removal of heavy metals from water; breakdown of sewage effluent; breakdown of crude oil, tar and petroleum products; biodegradation of plastics

A large waste tip, Manila, Philippines

4.2 CELL AND TISSUE CULTURES

The production of useful products, based on the mass cultivation of viruses or living material, normally passes through three stages:

Laboratory model → pilot plant → industrial plant

In the laboratory, the primary objective is to discover the optimum conditions for the growth and reproduction of the material that is to be cultured. These optimal conditions must be defined in terms of nutrient supply, oxygen supply, temperature and pH. Beyond that, a researcher may need to know the mean generation time (see p. 00), the rate at which nutrients are used up, the stage at which useful metabolites are produced, and the volume of gas generated by the cells or tissues as they grow. Needless to say, viruses, micro-organisms, plant cells and animal cells all have different requirements and mutliply at different rates.

Viruses are required in large numbers for the production of vaccines, or for use as cloning vectors. They present a particular problem, because they cannot multiply outside a living host cell. Bacteriophages may be grown relatively easily on bacterial cultures, either in liquid or on semi-solid media. At one time animal viruses were grown in living animals such as rabbits, mice and guinea pigs. Others were grown in fertilised eggs, widely used in the production of anti-viral vaccines. The virus was injected into one of the embryonic membranes of the developing egg of a hen. Viral growth was indicated either by death of the embryo, or by damage to one or more of its membranes. Today, such methods have been largely replaced by growing animal viruses in animal cell cultures, contained in Carrel flasks (see Figure 48) or larger containers. Plant viruses are grown in cultures of plant plastids, which are plant cells from which the cell walls have been digested away.

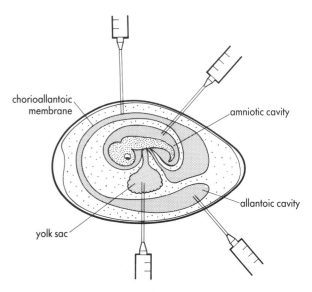

Figure 47   Regions in an fertilised egg, where viruses can be grown

Plant cells and tissues require media that contain the same macro-and micronutrients as are required by algae (see Table 3, p.23). In addition, as they cannot usually photosynthesise, they also require sucrose, organic nitrogen sources (e.g. glycine, inositol), vitamins (B_1, B_6 and nicotinic acid) and growth regulators (e.g. auxin, cytokinin and gibberellic acid). Casein hydrolysate (peptide source), yeast extract (vitamin source) and a gelling agent, either agar or gelatin, may be added to media.

Animal cells, especially cells from mammalian tissues, are particularly demanding when grown in culture. They require a supply of complex nutrients, similar to those required by fungi, and a steady supply of oxygen. The growth media must also be buffered, to keep the pH between 7.1 and 7.4, contain additional vitamins, and have the same water potential as the cell cytoplasm, equivalent to a 0.9 per cent solution of NaCl. At the beginning of this century, cells from a frog embryo were grown in clotted lymph. Concurrently, other excised animal tissues were cultured in media containing blood plasma and embryo sac fluid. A wide selection of media, such as Liebig's meat extract, is now available for culturing animal tissues. Figure 48 shows the

(a) *Sources*

ADULT   EMBRYO   EGG

(b) *Dissection*

scalpel

(c) *Enzyme digestion/ mechanical separation*

(e) *Further dissection*

enzyme solution

magnet

(d) *Cell culture*

(f) *Primary explants*

(g) *Organ culture*

carrel flask

cell monolayer

Figure 48   *Stages in preparing animal cell, tissue and organ cultures*

three basic techniques that are used to prepare cell culture, primary explants and organ cultures from animals:

   (i) **Cell cultures** consist of suspensions of separate cells, obtained by the enzymatic and mechanical disruption of a tissue. These cells may be cultured in a suspension in a liquid medium, or as an adherent monolayer on a solid substratum. Skin cells, for example, grow best on a flat, rough surface, in a shallow depth of liquid medium.

 (ii) **Primary explants** are small pieces of tissue, from which new cells form and break away to form either a suspension or adherent monolayer.

(iii) **Organ cultures** are larger pieces of tissue, in which the structural and functional organisation of cells is maintained, at least in part.

These three tissue culture techniques have been adopted into many routine applications, including the production of monoclonal antibodies, chromosome analysis and the study of animal viruses.

4.3 SCALING UP

Modifying a laboratory procedure, so that it can be used on an industrial scale, is called 'scaling up'. Laboratory procedures are normally scaled up via intermediate models of increasing size (Figure 49). The larger the plant, the greater the running costs, as skilled people are required to monitor and maintain the machinery.

Large industrial fermenters have to be built to high specifications. Containment of the desired micro-organism, and exclusion of any contaminating organism, is the first objective. Of almost equal importance is installing highly sensitive controls that allow pH, temperature and fluid volume to be maintained within narrow limits. Foam formation, at the surface of the culture broth, must also be monitored and controlled.

As cells multiply in the culture broth, the mixture becomes more viscous. This increasing **viscosity**, as cells multiply, can pose serious mechanical problems. Both the motor, and the paddles that it drives, must be large enough to

Figure 49　Scaling up

rotate and stir the mixture, even when it reaches a porridge-like consistency. At this stage, when the mixture becomes thick and sticky, cells tend to stick to the sides of the vessel and surface of the paddles. These surfaces have either to be non-adhesive themselves, or coated with a non-adhesive substance, to overcome the problem of cell adhesion.

In cultures of aerobic organisms, **oxygen supply** is the most important limiting factor. For large-scale cultures, forced aeration with small bubbles having a high surface area to volume ratio, is the only way in which the high oxygen demand of cells can be met. Sterile air must therefore be pumped into the container, entering via a 'sparger' with multiple small holes. Micro-organisms and other cells, contained in a confined space, generate heat as they grow. This must be removed via a heat exchanger in order to maintain a constant temperature. The larger the number of cells in a container, the greater the risk of spoilage through **cell mutations** and contamination with undesirable plasmids. In **batch cultures**, when cells are grown in a fixed volume of a liquid medium in a closed vessel, without making any additions or removals during the period of incubation, the actual time taken for incubation is influenced by the shape and volume of the container. When cells are grown in **continuous culture**, with nutrients added and cells harvested at a given steady rate, the shape and volume of the container also infuences the rate at which the process can be operated. The principal of continuous culture is shown in Figure 50.

It should be noted that the term 'fermentation' is now applied to industrial processes that are oxygen-independent (anaerobic) as well as to those that are oxygen-dependent (aerobic).

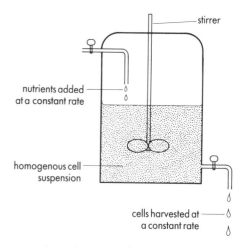

Figure 50　A continuous culture system (e.g. chemostat)

4.4 FERMENTERS

Large-scale fermentations, both areobic and anaerobic, are carried out in large cylindrical steel containers, commonly called **bioreactors** or **fermenters**. Apart form being able to withstand the high internal pressures resulting from gas production, stainless steel provides a smooth, hard and corrosive-resistant inner surface, from which micro-organisms can be removed by washing. After the inner surface has been disinfected, and washed with distilled water, the central cavity is filled to a specified level with a sterile nutrient solution. This nutrient fluid is then inoculated with a pure culture of a bacterium or fungus. **Paddles**, driven by a motor, rotate the mixture at about 1000 rpm, so that the cell or mycelium suspension is always homogenous. As nutrients are used up, more are added from the nutrient feed pipe, especially in continuous cultures. There may also be an inlet point for alkali – to counteract increasing acidity as fermentation proceeds – and 'antifoam', to prevent the formation of surface froth. **Electrically-operated probes** monitor the formation of foam at the surface of the mixture and changes in temperature, pH and oxygen concentration within it. A **water jacket**, surrounding the fermenter, normally contains fast-flowing cold water, used to cool the fermenter since fermentation is a heat-generating (exothermic) process. In a batch process, superheated water at around 120°C may be pumped through the two steam inlets between one batch and the next in order to sterilise the inner surface of the fermenter.

Although some 'fermentations' operate anaerobically, the vast majority are aerobic processes, requiring large volumes of filtered air or pure oxygen. Air entering a fermenter needs to be filtered, otherwise air-borne micro-organisms may enter the culture and produce foreign products that would affect the purity of the end products.

After it has been filtered, air enters the bottom of the fermenter via a **sparger**. This is either a multiholed steel ring or a perforated disc, from which bubbles rise through the mixture. Most of the air, together with carbon dioxide and other gases produced by cell metabolism, leave the fermenter via an exhaust pipe positioned above the liquid level. As the fermenter is operated under pressure it requires a **pressure gauge** and **safety valve** to prevent dangerous build up of pressure, which could lead to an explosion. At the end of fermentation, when the biomass of cells or mycelia has increased, surplus material may be removed from the fermenter via a **harvest pipe**.

Two variations in fermenter vessel design are shown in Figure 52. In a **draught-tube airlift vessel**, a smaller stainless steel cylinder is positioned inside a larger one. Incoming air or oxygen carries the cell suspension upwards. It completes its circulation by returning between the walls of the two cylinders. **Looped airlift vessels**, used for the production of single cell protein (p.64) and mycoprotein (p.65), have two vertical shafts, a 'riser' and 'downcomer'. An upward draft of air or oxygen from the bottom of the 'riser' causes the contents to rise. At the top of the vessel, after gas has entered the exhaust pipe, solid material sinks down the 'downcomer' under the action of gravity. Neither of these two designs requires a motor or paddles.

Figure 52 *Alternative fermentation vessels*

Figure 51   An aerobic fermenter

4.5 DOWNSTREAM PROCESSING

Downstream processing, or **'downstreaming'**, is the extraction and purification of the desired end products of fermentation processes. Such products might include cells, solvents or solutes. Various processes are available for the separation of cells from the fermentation broth in which they are grown, including flocculation, filtration, centrifugation, sedimentation or flotation. The procedure adopted depends on whether it is the cells, or the solution surrounding them, that contains the desired end products. Downstreaming to extract cells from liquid cultures may involve the following successive stages:

Flocculation
(to precipitate cells)

↓

Filtration
(to separate cells from solution)

↓

Centrifugation
(to concentrate cell masses)

↓

Drying
(to prepare cells for packaging)

If the solution surrounding the cells is required, as in brewing, or one of the solutes is the required product, as in antibiotic production, any of the following downstream processes might be used:

Flocculation
(to precipitate cells)

↓

Ultrafiltration
Centrifugation or
(to obtain a cell-free solution)

↓

Distillation
(to concentrate the solvent, or drive it off)

↓

Drying
(to obtain crude solute)

↓

Purification
(to obtain pure solute)

(a) *Spray drying*

(b) *Fluidised bed drying*

(c) *Freeze drying*

Figure 53   Methods of drying cellular products – a stage in downstream processing

Later in this book you will find detailed accounts of downstreaming in the production of beer (p.59) and penicillin (p.70).

QUESTIONS

1 The diagram below illustrates a large industrial fermenter.

a) Name the parts A–G.
b) Through which parts do sterile materials enter the fermenter?
c) Explain the function of part C.
d) How is part A affected as cell density increases inside the fermenter?
e) Why are the walls of the fermenter usually made from stainless steel?
f) Name two other types of fermenter commonly used in industrial processes.

2 Biotechnologists aim to improve the quality of water by (i) removing heavy metals and (ii) speeding up the rate at which sewage effluent is broken down. For each of the following, state two aims or achievements of biotechnologists:
a) Cereal crops
b) Brewing
c) House plants
d) Vaccines
e) Food colourings
f) Human proteins
g) Therapeutic enzymes
h) Mining
i) Oil extraction
j) Oil pollution
k) Fuel production
l) Biosensors

3 What do you understand by the term 'biotechnology'?
Evaluate the contributions of a) biologists and b) chemical engineers in developing modern biotechnology.

4 What
a) nutritional and
b) environmental conditions are required to grow a bacterium such as *E. coli* in the laboratory?
In what ways do the requirements of
c) viruses and
d) algae differ from those of bacteria?
When large numbers of cells are grown in fermenters, what factors must be monitored and regulated?
How is this monitoring and regulation achieved?

5 Draw and describe the gross structure and component parts of a large industrial fermenter. Outline the methods that can be used to separate and purify
a) liquid and
b) solid end products of fermentation processes.

BIBLIOGRAPHY

Biotechnology and chemical engineering

Brown, CM, Campbell, I and Priest, F G (1987) *Introduction to Biotechnology* Blackwell Scientific Publications
Higgins, IJ, Best, DJ and Jones, J (1985) *Biotechnology, Principles and Applications* Blackwell Scientific Publications
Mantell, SH, Matthews, JA and McKee, RA (1985) *Principles of Plant Biotechnology* Blackwell Scientific Publications
Mantell, SH and Smith, H eds (1983) *Plant Biotechnology* Cambridge University Press
Marx, JL (1989) *A Revolution in Biotechnology* Cambridge University Press
Prentis, S (1984) *Biotechnology: A New Industrial Revolution* Orbis
Olejnik, I and Farmer, B (1988) *Biology and Industry* Blackie
Primrose, SB (1987) *Modern Biotechnology* Blackwell Scientific Publications
Sattelle, DB (1988) *Biotechnology in Perspective* Hobsons Publishing
Smith, JE (1981) *Biotechnology* (Studies in Biology No. 136) Edward Arnold
Stanbury, P F and Whittaker, A (1984) *Principles of Fermentation Technology* Permagon Press

FOODS AND DRINKS

Bread-making, wine-making and cheese-making are ancient crafts, all dependent on the activities of micro-organisms. In the 20th century these crafts have been transformed into industrial processes allowing the controlled production of foods and drinks on a large scale, and achieving a more predictable end product. In the industrialised countries, biotechnologists have improved the techniques of food processing and developed microbial strains better suited to the jobs that they perform. A future aim of biotechnology is to produce more food that is inexpensive and has a high nutritional value. One way forward may be to produce single cell protein (SCP), prepared from the cells or hyphae of micro-organisms. The fact that many micro-organisms can double their biomass in a day is an attractive feature, promising both rapid and abundant food production in the future. Conversely, SCP production is expensive and some of the end products aren't particularly palatable.

The following sections outline stages in the manufacture of bread, beer, dairy products and other foods that depend on micro-organisms for their production.

5.1 BREAD

The principal dry ingredients used in bread-making are wheat flour, salt, sugar, ascorbic acid, and the yeast *Saccharomyces cerevisiae*. Water or milk is added to produce a thick, sticky dough which is repeatedly folded or **kneaded**, to create nuclei for gas production and expansion. The mixed dough is rested, folded, and moulded into tins. In a humid atmosphere at 34–35°C dough is left for 10 minutes to 'prove'. It is then remoulded and left for a final 'proving'.

During the 'proving' process, fermentation of sugars in the dough, catalysed by enzymes from the yeast cells, produces carbon dioxide. As this gas cannot escape from the sticky mass, it fills the gas nuclei and causes the dough to 'rise', or increase in volume. This process is sometimes called **leavening**. Ascorbic acid (vitamin C) makes gluten in the dough more elastic. As a result, the time required for leavening is greatly reduced, an important consideration in commercial bread production. While the dough is being leavened, proteolytic enzymes from the yeast act on proteins in the flour, changing their textures by making them less tough and stringy. The overall effects of leavening are to make the dough lighter, more digestible and of better flavour, following from the production of organic acids, alcohols and esters by yeast cells.

The role of enzymes in the process may be summarised as follows:

(i) Maltose (in flour) $\xrightarrow[\text{(from yeast)}]{\text{maltase}}$ glucose

(ii) Sucrose (added) $\xrightarrow[\text{(from yeast)}]{\text{invertase}}$ glucose + fructose

(iii) Glucose + fructose $\xrightarrow[\text{(from yeast)}]{\text{'zymase'}}$ alcohol + carbon dioxide

Baking inactivates the yeast, drives off any alcohol that may be present in the dough, and stops enzymic reactions. The bubbles of carbon dioxide persist, however, giving the bread a spongy texture after baking. Genetic engineers are currently attempting to improve strains of yeast used in baking. Their main aims are to produce more active, better flavoured strains, which can make dough rise at lower temperatures, and in less time.

Table 7 Ingredients for bread-making

INGREDIENTS	PARTS (VOLUME)
Flour	100
Salt	1
Sugar	1
Yeast	5
Ascorbic acid (vitamin C)	0.5
Milk or water	60

THE LIBRARY
GUILDFORD COLLEGE
of Further and Higher Education

(a) *Mixing*   (b) *Kneading*   (c) *1st moulding*   (d) *1st proving*

flour + fat
+ salt + yeast
+ water

dough

(e) *2nd moulding*   (f) *2nd proving*   (g) *Baking*   (h) *Cooling*   (i) *Wrapping*

Figure 54   Commercial bread production

5.2 BEERS AND WINES

Beer

Beer is produced from barley grains, which contain mostly starch and proteins. There are six major stages in the manufacture of beer, as follows:

Malting

↓

Milling

↓

Mashing

↓

Boiling

↓

Fermentation

↓

Finishing

Malting results in the conversion of starch to maltose, and proteins to amino acids. This is achieved by steeping the dry grains in water, then layering them in a malting tower or spreading them out on a malthouse floor, and allowing them

Brewing: using yeast to ferment 'wort'

59

to germinate until their roots have reached about 0.5–0.75 cm in length (Figure 55). Enzymes produced during germination, namely amylases and proteases, degrade stored materials in the grains into compounds that can be fermented by yeast. Germination is stopped by slowly heating the grains at 80°C, a temperature that is sufficient to destroy the enzymes. The grains that emerge from this process are known as malted barley.

Milling breaks each malted barley grain into 2–3 pieces. These crushed grains, or grist, are then fed into a 'mash tun', where **mashing** takes place. Hot water percolates through the grains, softening them, and extracting a nutrient-rich liquid called 'wort'.

Boiling is a stage in which 'wort', mixed with hops to give added flavour and some antiseptic properties, is heated to a high temperature in a 'lauter tun'. The resulting sterile liquid, after straining through a 'hop-back', is then allowed to cool.

Fermentation takes place in large conical fermenters, after an appropriate strain of yeast has been added. As the fermentation of the beer proceeds, *S. cerevisiae* builds up at the bottom of the fermenter and at the surface of the 'wort', where it forms a crust. Carbon dioxide is prevented from escaping and so dissolves in the beer, making it effervesce. After 7–10 days fermentation is complete. Downstreaming consists of flocculation, filtration and maturation. A protein called isinglass, from the swim bladders of tropical fish, is added to flocculate yeast cells. Isinglass, which has an opposite electric charge to that of the yeast cells, causes yeast to be precipitated as a firm deposit, leaving an almost clear liquid.

Filtration, through a slurry of diatomite rock (fossilised silica shells of diatoms), layered to form a bed, removes any yeast cells that may remain in suspension. Following filtration the beer is allowed to stand for several weeks at 0°C, until any cell debris or protein haze has cleared.

Finishing, the final stage in beer production consists of packaging beer for sale to the public. Bottled and canned beers are usually pasteurised

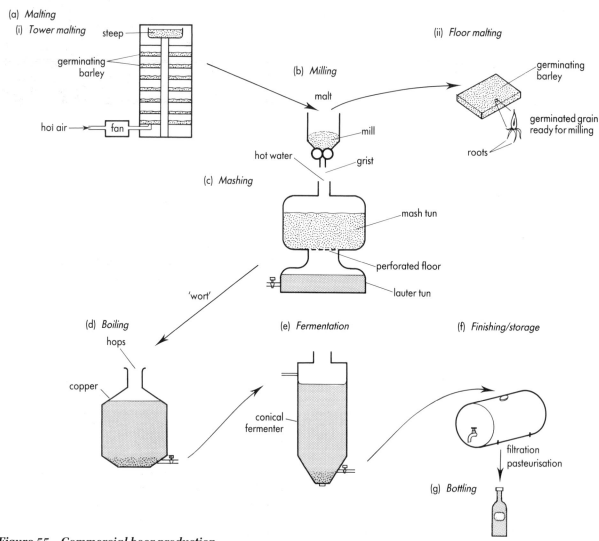

Figure 55   Commercial beer production

Malting barley

Hops in flower

at 60°C to kill off any yeast cells that may still be present. Some beer is still marketed in wooden barrels, where interactions with the wood give it a more mellow flavour. In general, the alcohol (ethanol) content of beer is around 4–6% volume 'Low alcohol' beer may either be processed, to remove most of the alcohol by osmosis, or a direct product of an engineered strain of yeast that produces alcohol in low concentration.

Wines

Wines are traditionally made from grapes, but can also be made from sugar-rich fruits, flowers or root crops, such as parsnips or carrots. In commercial winemaking, grapes are crushed between rollers then passed into a fermenting vat. Here sulphur dioxide – to prevent the growth of unwanted micro-organisms – and yeast are added. The resulting fermented pulp, known as 'must', passes through a press, where seeds and skins are removed. Finally, following retention in one or more settling vats, the fermented juice is filtered, heated and aged before bottling.

Table wines contain from 6–12% alcohol. Fortified wines, such as sherry, may contain as much as 20% alcohol. Spirits, including whisky and vodka, the products of distillation, contain 30% or more alcohol.

5.3 VINEGAR

Vinegar, used to flavour food, contains not less that 4% acetic acid. It is produced by a second fermentation of beer, cider or wine. The second fermentation is aerobic and dependent on a mixed culture of *Acetobacter*, including *A. scheutzenbachii, A. curium* and *A. orleanse*. Providing oxygen is available, these bacteria convert alcohol to acetic acid by the following route:

Alcohol (ethanol) → acetaldehyde → acetic acid

Commercial vinegar producers generally increase the alcohol content of the beer (for malt vinegar) or cider (for cider vinegar) to about 12%. In the traditional vinegar-making process, large wooden vats, made of columbian pine, were fitted with many bundles of birch twigs (Figure 56). Bacteria on the surface of these twigs converted alcohol-enriched beer or cider to vinegar. After it had dripped over the surface of the twigs, the fermenting liquid was collected and recycled, so that it was sprayed over the twigs several times before it was removed and bottled. Today, however, most vinegar is made in aerated fermenters, similar to that shown in Figure 51.

Figure 56 Vinegar production by the traditional method

5.4 CHEESE

Cheese-making is an ancient craft, originally used to preserve milk from attack by micro-organisms that rendered it unfit for human consumption. More recently, however, it has developed into a biotechnology, drawing on specialised machinery, enzymology, microbiology and biochemistry. In both small and large-scale cheese-making there are four main steps, as follows:

Milk-pretreatment

↓

Milk coagulation

↓

Curd extraction

↓

Salting, pressing and ripening

Milk pretreatment consists of low temperature pasteurisation to kill off any micro-organisms that might be present. Milk coagulation is brought about by adding a 'starter culture', consisting of lactose-fermenting bacteria, and rennet, which

Table 8 Bacteria used in cheese-making

ROLE	SPECIES
Gas production	*Leuconostoc cremoris* *Leuconostoc lactis* *Lactococcus diacetylactis*
Acid production	*Streptococcus cremoris* *Streptococcus lactis*

causes the formation of a solid curd and liquid whey. Cheese is made from the curd, often salted, pressed and ripened before it is eaten. The bacteria used in cheese-making are either gas producers or acid producers. **Gas producers** release carbon dioxide, while **acid producers** form lactic acid from lactose. It is the gas producers that determine the texture of a cheese. Acid producers determine its flavour.

Cheddar cheese is made from milk sterilised at 72°C for at least 15 seconds. A starter consisting mostly of subspecies of *Streptococcus lactis* is added. About an hour after adding the starter, the milk is said to 'ripen', as its lactic acid content rises (to more than 0.18%). The milk is then ready for **renneting**. Rennet (previously called rennin) which is a mixture of chymosin and pepsin from the stomach of a calf (or from genetically-engineered bacteria), is added to coagulate casein, the principal milk protein. A semi-solid mass or 'coagulum' is formed, consisting of fat, water and solutes trapped in a casein matrix.

Next, the coagulum is cut into pea-sized pieces, so that it separates into small, creamy particles of curd, suspended in a watery whey. **Scalding** the mixture at a temperature of 30–39°C for about 45 minutes expels more whey, and changes the texture of the curd. After scalding the curd is allowed to settle under gravity, or **pitch**, and the whey is run off. At this stage the individual pieces of curd begin to knit together into blocks. The blocks are then cut, stacked, drained and turned in a process called **cheddaring**. When 'cheddaring' is complete, and pH has fallen to about 5.2, the curd is **milled** into small pieces. Salting is the final stage of preparation. The addition of salt to about 2% helps preserve the finished cheese and brings out its flavour.

Semi-soft cheeses (e.g. Brie, Camembert), hard cheeses (e.g. Lancashire) and very hard cheeses (e.g. Cheddar) are **pressed** to reduce their water content and bind the curd into a solid mass. The raw cheese is then moulded and usually coated with one or more layers of plastic, to conserve water and prevent colonisation by species of micro-organism living in the wild. **Ripening** consists of storing the cheese under appropriate conditions so that bacteria and other micro-

Blocks of cheese curd

organisms can cause chemical changes in the curd, improving and enhancing its flavour. Mould fungi are used in the ripening of some cheeses. Spores of *Penicillium camemberti* are sprayed over the surface of raw Camembert cheese. Those of *Penicillium roqueforti* are placed deep into the curd of Roquefort cheese by using special needles. The growth of fungal hyphae in cheese gives it a stronger, characteristic flavour.

5.5 YOGHURT

Two species of bacteria *Lactobacillus bulgaricus* and *Lactococcus thermophilus*, in approximately equal proportions, are used to make yoghurt. Commercial producers pasteurise and homogenise milk before adding the starter. After stirring, the mixture is then incubated for 3–6 hours at 40–45°C. At this temperature the two bacteria have a mutually stimulating effect on one another. Proteolytic enzymes from *L. bulgaricus* break down milk proteins into peptides. These stimulate growth of *L. thermophilus* which, in

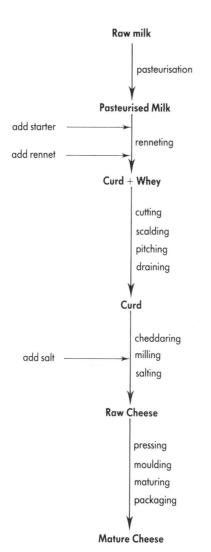

Figure 57   Stages in the manufacture of cheddar cheese

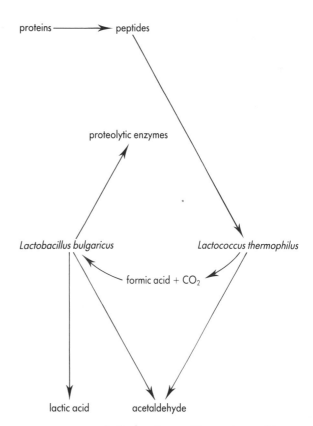

Figure 58   Metabolic products of bacteria used in yoghurt making

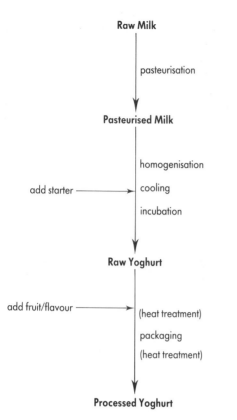

Raw Milk

↓ pasteurisation

Pasteurised Milk

↓ homogenisation

add starter ———→ cooling

incubation

↓

Raw Yoghurt

add fruit/flavour ———→ (heat treatment)

packaging

(heat treatment)

↓

Processed Yoghurt

Figure 59   Stages in the manufacture of processed yoghurt

Listeria monocytogenes (× 500), a food poisoning organism sometimes found in cheeses (see p.66)

turn, produce formic acid and carbon dioxide, growth stimulants for *L. bulgaricus*. As incubation proceeds, *L. bulgaricus* also converts lactose to lactic acid. At the end of incubation pH has fallen to around 4.2–4.4, and the lactic acid has coagulated proteins, causing the yoghurt to thicken. Acetaldehyde, a metabolic by-product of both species, gives raw yoghurt its characteristic flavour. Further processing may involve the addition of flavouring, colouring and fruit pulp. Some yoghurts may then receive additional heat treatment to kill off any living bacteria, before or after packaging for the consumer.

5.6 BUTTER

Butter is made from cream. During churning, tiny droplets of fat coalesce to turn a fat-in-water emulsion (cream) into a water-in-fat emulsion (butter). Rejection of the surplus watery solution, or buttermilk, leaves a solid product with 80% or more fat. There are two main types of butter, called 'sweet cream' and 'lactic'.

Sweet-cream butter, the most popular type, is prepared from pasteurised cream, cooled to between 4–5°C. The cream is then passed through a machine called a continuous buttermaker, where it is churned, separated and worked. Churning causes the globules of fat to aggregate into butter granules, while the watery buttermilk is drawn off. The butter granules are then worked to reduce their water content, and compressed into blocks of the desired consistency. Salt, in the form of a slurry, may be added before the final working.

Lactic butter is made from fermented cream. After pasteurisation, a starter is added which contains *Streptococcus lactis*, a diacetyl-producing bacterium, *Leuconostoc citrovorum* or *Leuconostoc dextranicum*. Fermentation by *S. lactis* produces lactic acid, with citric acid as a byproduct. The second bacterium in the starter acts on citric acid, converting it to diacetyl, the compound which gives butter its characteristic flavour. Butter should be kept cool, dark and away from strongly flavoured foods. Exposure to light causes oxidation of some fats, reduces the vitamin A content, and may leave the butter with a rancid flavour. For this reason butter is often wrapped in aluminium foil, which excludes light and protects the product from foreign flavours and odours.

5.7 SINGLE CELL PROTEIN (SCP)

Single cell proteins (SCPs) are the whole dried cells of bacteria, fungi or algae grown in mass culture. In addition to a high protein content, forming 40% or more of their total dry mass, SCPs have a high content of amino acids, vitamins, lipids, carbohydrates, minerals and nucleic acids. They are used mostly as animal feedstuffs, because humans find the cell walls indigestible and cannot metabolise the high nucleic acid (purine) content.

The basis of SCP production is the continuous culture (or fermentation) of micro-organisms under carefully controlled conditions. In the early 1970s ICI produced SCP from a bacterium called *Methylophilus methylotrophus,* with methanol as the carbon source and ammonia as the sole source of nitrogen. Methanol was chosen because it was relatively abundant, miscible with water, and easily separated from the end product. The fermenter had two vertical shafts, a 'riser' and 'downcomer', through which the contents circulated. Sterilised methanol with dissolved nutrients entered at the bottom of the 'riser'. Bubbles of air and ammonia, entering at the base of the 'riser', assisted the upward flow of cells. At the top of the fermenter bacterial cells, in the form of a cream, were extracted. This extract was flocculated by steam treatment and centrifugation, then dried. After extensive toxicity testing the product was sold as animal feed under the name *Pruteen*. Unfortunately, high production costs made this SCP more expensive than soy bean and fish meal. These economic problems caused the plant to close down in the early 1980s.

One of the earliest uses of a yeast for SCP production was by British Petroleum, again in the 1970's. They used *Candida lipolytica*, with n-paraffins as the carbon source. Today, most SCP production is in South America, where yeasts are grown for animal foodstuffs and human consumption. In the future it is possible that algae and cyanobacteria, such as *Spirulina*, first used by the Aztecs to make cakes, may become major sources of SCPs. The fact that these organisms have a rapid growth rate, and require only water and mineral salt as nutrients, makes them particularly attractive as food sources, especially in tropical and sub-tropical regions. Furthermore, the dried product promises to be more palatable and digestible than bacterial SCP.

Growing micro-organisms for food has two attractions:

(i) They have a much faster growth rate than agricultural products, with a doubling time measured in hours.

(ii) A wide range of waste materials can be used as substrates, including cheese whey, molasses and starchy wastes.

These advantages, however, have to be balanced against high production costs and the fact that some of the end products are unacceptable to humans, because they are indigestible, bitter-tasting and can cause gout on account of their high RNA content. Perhaps the most promising and commercially successful SCP is **myco-protein**, a meat substitute made from hyphae of the fungus *Fusarium graminearum*.

The fungus is grown in a looped air-lift fermenter at 30°C, in a liquid medium containing glucose syrup, mineral salts and choline, a growth factor that increases the length of the hyphae. Continuously harvested from the fermenter the hyphae, pass into an RNA reduction vessel, where heating to 64°C reduces the RNA content to around 1% of total dry mass. The processed hyphae are then cut, coloured and flavoured to resemble meat. The end product, marketed as 'Quorn', is often added to meat products such as sausages, where it blends well with the other ingredients. As Table 9 shows, myco-protein contains less fat and more fibre than beef, important considerations for those seeking a more healthy diet.

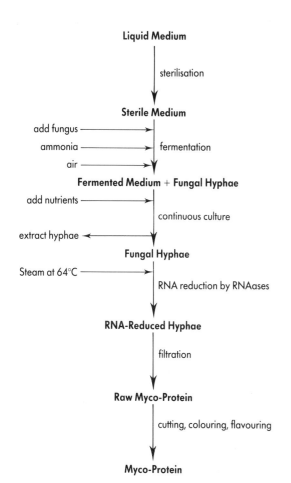

Figure 60   Stages in myco-protein production

Table 9   Essential nutrients in myco-protein and beef

NUTRIENT	% DRY MASS	
	Myco-protein	Beef
Protein	40–45	60–65
Fat	10–15	30–40
Mineral salts	3–4	1–2
Fibre	30–40	None

5.8 FOOD PRESERVATION

Developing effective methods of food storage and preservation helped humans abandon their original nomadic existence as hunter-gatherers. Today, large human populations, like those in the UK, are heavily dependent on effective methods of food preservation. Untreated food always contains some saprophytic organisms, notably bacteria and fungi, capable of causing 'food spoilage'. In addition, some pathogens – the direct or indirect cause of 'food poisoning' – may also be present. If food is stored under conditions in which these micro-organisms can multiply, populations of pathogens may build up to dangerous levels. Most food poisoning organisms, including species of *Salmonella*, *Campylobacter fetus* and *Listeria monocytogenes*, multiply inside the human gut. **Endotoxins**, the cause of diarrhoea, vomiting and fever, are released when these bacteria are engulfed by phagocytes inside the human intestine. Other bacteria, such as *Clostridium botulinum* and *Staphylococcus aureus* multiply in the food that they colonise, and poison it by releasing extracellular **exotoxins**. Anyone eating food containing these exotoxins becomes ill, although they may not necessarily swallow any of the bacteria that have produced them.

Today, the most widely used methods of preserving food are refrigeration (freezing), heat treatment (sterilisation), chemical inhibition and drying. In the future, irradiation with gamma rays may gain popularity.

5.8.1 Refrigeration and freezing

Household refrigerators, kept at about 4°C, reduce the growth rate and reproduction of most bacterial pathogens. Freezers, at about −20°C, prevent all known pathogens from growing or multiplying. In fact, at this temperature populations of bacteria in deep-frozen foods slowly decline. Even so, neither refrigeration nor freezing kills all the bacteria present in a food sample. On thawing, any bacteria in the food are reactivated and often multiply at an increased rate, because freezing has broken down cell walls and increased the food's water content.

Vegetable, meat and fish products are heat-treated before freezing to kill off all of their natural microflora, and denature enzymes that might otherwise cause spoilage. An increase in the popularity of chilled straight-from-the-supermarket meals has been accompanied by an increase in infections caused by *Salmonella*, *Campylobacter* and *Listeria*. This has happened because these species grow relatively well at low temperatures in the range 0–15°C. If supermarket chilling cabinets are faulty, allowing temperatures to rise above 5°C, or if the food is allowed to warm up slowly after purchase, the public is at risk from these organisms. This is especially so in food that has passed its 'sell by' date.

5.8.2 Heat treatment

Exposure to temperature in the range 70–100°C for 15–60 seconds kills most bacteria. Milk, for example, is pasteurised by heating at 72°C for 15 seconds. This temperature is sufficient to denature enzymes and kill bacteria, but it doesn't noticeably affect the milk's flavour.

Canned meats, fruits and vegetables are packed into containers, sealed to the air, and heated to a temperature of around 120°C. This temperature is sufficient to kill off any bacteria in the food, together with heat-resistant **endospores** of species such as *Clostridium botulinum*. The product remains sterile until the can is opened, but it is then colonised by micro-organisms from the environment.

5.8.3 Chemical inhibition

Growth of pathogens in food is rare below pH 5.0. For this reason lactic, sulphurous and benzoic acids are added to certain foods and beverages to lower their pH. A number of sodium salts and antibiotics have been used to slow the growth rates of bacteria and fungi, and to prevent germination of their spores. These chemicals include sodium nitrite, sodium chloride, sodium metabisulphite, sodium sorbate benzoate, and the antibiotics nicin and tylosin.

When bacon is cured, the meat is injected with a solution of sodium chloride, sodium nitrate, potassium nitrate and polyphosphate, followed by steeping in a similar solution. Salt-tolerant micrococci and lactobacilli reduce nitrate to nitrite. They also assist in the formation of nitrosomyoglobin in muscles, which gives the bacon its attractive pink colour. As an additional treatment, the bacon may then be smoked. Wood smoke contains acids and other chemicals with bactericidal effects. Hence the ancient practice of smoking meat, fish and cheese has been up-dated. Volatile fatty acids from the treated foods are thought to contribute to their preservation, inhibiting all but lactic acid bacteria.

5.8.4 Drying

Cereals, pulses and potato products are some of the commonest food items stored for long periods in a dry form. A total water content of below 10–15% inhibits the growth of micro-organisms and prevents enzymes from causing spoilage. Placing fruits in a concentrated solution of sugar, or meat in a concentrated solution of salt, has a similar drying effect. Water is drawn by osmosis from any micro-organisms in the food, so that they are left with insufficient water for growth or reproduction.

5.8.5 Irradiation

Irradiation with gamma rays, which can be carried out after products have been packaged for final distribution, is a powerful technique for killing micro-organisms. Applied to dairy products, cooked poultry, meat and shellfish, it would virtually eliminate food poisoning caused by *Salmonella*, *Campylobacter* and *Listeria*, along with other bacteria that produce endotoxins. Irradiation also extends the shelf-life of fresh vegetables and fruits, keeping strawberries in prime condition for as long as three weeks. Used to treat grain products, dried herbs and spices, irradiation can provide an alternative to the use of insecticides. Usefully, irradiation also prevents stored onions and potatoes from sprouting.

Although irradiated food does not itself become radioactive, the treatment nevertheless causes some nutrients to undergo irreversible changes. Vitamins are destroyed, along with essential fatty acids. A number of untested toxic, mutagenic and carcinogenic agents may be formed. Work on laboratory animals, fed exclusively on irradiated food, has suggested possible long-term damage to the immune system and kidneys, with an increase in genetic disorders of the blood.

Table 10   The advantages and disadvantages of irradiated food

ADVANTAGES	DISADVANTAGES
Reduces risk of food poisoning from endotoxin-producing bacteria	Doesn't reduce risk of food poisoning from exotoxin-producing bacteria
Improved texture and flavour in some foods (e.g. chicken, meat, certain cheeses)	Adverse effects on texture and flavour in some foods (e.g. cucumber)
Longer shelf life	Loss of vitamins and essential fatty acids
	Could be used to disguise old and dirty food
	Formation of toxic chemicals?

At the present time 21 countries permit food irradiation. Clearly, the technique is still experimental. If irradition food is a health hazard, any damage may take from 10–20 years before it shows up. A more immediate worry to health authorities and consumers, however, is the possibility that stale food, with a high bacterial count, could be irradiated to resemble fresh food.

QUESTIONS

1 Fermentation of glucose to alcohol may be represented by the following equation:
$$C_6H_{12}O_6 \rightarrow 2C_2H_5OH + 2CO_2$$
Glucose   Alcohol   Carbon dioxide
$(H=1, C=12, O=16)$
  a) From the equation
      (i) Calculate the theoretical yield of alcohol from 1 kg glucose.
      (ii) What is the theoretical yield of carbon dioxide from the same mass of glucose?
      (iii) How much glucose would have been fermented to produce 1 dm^3 alcohol? What assumption has been made?
  b) Why should the home-brewer always ferment 'wort' in thick-walled glass vessels or plastic containers, never in beer bottles?
  c) What safety precautions should home-brewers take to prevent their beer being contaminated by other micro-organisms before, during and after fermentation?
  d) After fermentation is complete, beer may be treated with
      (i) pectolytic enzymes and
      (ii) filtered.
          Explain the reasons for each treatment.

2 Give a step-by-step account of modern beer production. In what ways does the large-scale production of wine differ from that of beer?

3 Outline the principal stages in the production of a commercial cheese such as cheddar. Explain the role of micro-organisms, including fungi, in cheese-making.

4 Write illustrated notes on each of the following:
  a) single cell protein (SCP)
  b) yoghurt production
  c) vinegar production
  d) bread-making

5 What methods are used to preserve food from attack by saprophytes? Explain the biological principles that make each of these methods effective in food preservation.
  Argue the case for and against the use of gamma ray irradiation as a method of food preservation.

BIBLIOGRAPHY

Foods and drinks

Barnell, HR (1980) *Biology of the Food Industry* (Studies in Biology No. 45) Edward Arnold

Bravery, HE (1976) *Home Booze* Book Club Associates, London

Goldblith, SA, Rey, L and Rothmeyer, W W eds (1984) *Freezedrying and Advanced Food Technology* Academic Press

Hough, JS (1984) *The Biotechnology and Malting Brewing* Cambridge University Press

National Dairy Council (1988) *From Farm to Doorstep: a Guide to Milk and Dairy Products*

Thear, K (1983) *Home Dairying* Batsford, London

6 CLINICAL AND FORENSIC MEDICINE

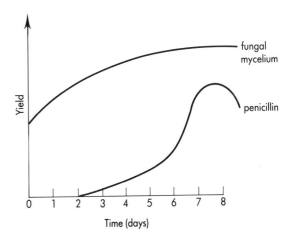

Recent advances in biotechnology promise major advances in many different areas of medicine. Mass cell culture techniques, pioneered in the production of antibiotics, are proving equally effective in producing a wide range of other pharmaceutical products. Hormones, vaccines and therapeutic proteins such as monoclonal antibodies and interferon are some of the cell products that are already being mass produced. An alternative approach is to use transgenic animals as a drug source. Transgenic animals are those which have genes transferred into them from another organism. Sheep that secrete interferon into their milk, and chickens that produce antibodies in their eggs, could soon become commonplace.

Our ability to manipulate the human genome has led to new diagnostic and therapeutic methods. Gene probes, added to treated blood samples or amniotic fluid from around a developing foetus, can diagnose the presence of viral, bacterial or other pathogens. They can also be used in the diagnosis of genetic disorders such as sickle cell anaemia, cystic fibrosis and Tay-Sachs disease. Gene therapy may soon provide a cure for some of these conditions, by replacing defective genes with normal ones. Genetic fingerprinting, in which an individual's identity can be established from analysis of the DNA in a person's blood or semen, is a powerful tool in forensic science.

6.1 ANTIBIOTICS

Antibiotics are antimicrobial compounds produced by living micro-organisms, mostly actinomycetes and mould fungi. They are among the **secondary metabolites** of these micro-organisms, synthesised late in the growth cycle (Figure 61). Today, therapeutically active antibiotics are widely used in clinical medicine and have saved many thousands of lives. Penicillin and streptomycin, that will destroy only a few species of bacteria, are known as

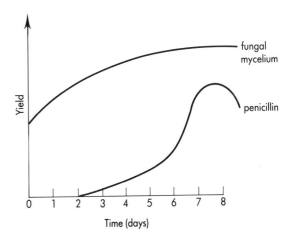

Figure 61   Penicillin production during a batch culture

Penicillium notatum × 225

The inhibition of unidentified bacteria by antibiotic pellets at the centre of each dish

narrow spectrum antibiotics. Conversely, tetracycline and chloramphenicol, effective against a wide range of organisms, are **broad spectrum antibiotics**. Elsewhere, outside medicine, antibiotics have many uses in the food industry, agriculture and research.

Penicillin

Penicillin was discovered by Alexander Fleming at St. Mary's Hospital, London in 1928–29. He noted that gram-positive bacteria, such as *Streptococcus sp.*, were killed by the diffusate from a colony of the mould fungus *Penicillium notatum*, an accidental contaminant of the culture plate. He called the active compound 'penicillin'. The subsequent extraction, purification and increase in the yield that made commercial production possible took almost another 20 years. Pioneer work was carried out by Howard Florey and Ernst Chain, based in Oxford, while in the USA techniques for large scale production were developed. 'Cornsteep liquor', a byproduct of starch manufacture from maize, was used as a nutrient.

By the early 1950s penicillin yields of about 60 mg/dm^3 fungus-nutrient mixture were being obtained. At about this time *P. notatum* was replaced by *Penicillium chrysogenum*, a species that produced more penicillin and was more suited to culture in large scale fermenters. As a result of mutation (induced by UV light and X rays), genetic manipulation, recombination and selection, geneticists had engineered a strain of the fungus that by the 1980's was producing yields of about 20 g/dm^3 fungus-nutrient mixture.

In response to the enormous demand for penicillin, modern production is carried out in fermenters (p.54) with a capacity of up to 200 000dm^3.

The fungus is grown in liquid culture, fed with nutrient solution and aerated. Batch culture is preferred, because contamination by any other micro-organisms or toxins, is extremely difficult to remove from the mixture, and can severely depress the yield. Optimal yields of penicillin are obtained after each batch has been cultured for 6 – 8 days (Figure 61). Separating out the penicillin involves filtration, continuous counter-current extraction, concentration and the addition of potassium compounds to precipitate crystals. The end product is benzyl penicillin, a relatively safe antibiotic with few serious side effects on those who take it. Even so, in this form the drug can be administered internally only by injection, because it is broken down and made ineffective by stomach acid. Producing a form of the drug that could be taken orally, such as **ampicillin**, was achieved partly by a combination of microbial and chemical syntheses, as the following sequence shows:

Benzyl penicillin (degraded by digestive enzymes) $\xrightarrow{\text{Fermented by } Kluyvera \; citrophila}$ 6–aminopenicillanic acid (6–APA)

Fermented by *Pseudomonas melanogenum* + DL–phenylglycine $\longrightarrow$ Ampicillin (absorbed into blood stream via intestine)

Thousands of different antibiotics are currently in use as drugs. Many, like penicillin, are used to treat acute bacterial infections. Others, as Table 11 shows, are used to combat fungal infections or slow the rate of tumour growth. Those antibiotics that kill bacterial by inhibiting cell wall synthesis are relatively safe drugs, because human cells are not usually damaged by them. Many of the others, though, that work by inhibiting protein synthesis or damaging cell membranes, can also damage human cells. As bacteria and tumour cells multiply faster than healthy human cells, they are most vulnerable to this group of antibiotics. The human cells survive longer because they have slower rates of transcription and translation, and in some cases, are less permeable to the antibiotics.

penicillin, cephalosporin and cycloserine inhibit cell wall synthesis

streptomycin, chloramphenicol, tetracycline and erythromycin inhibit protein synthesis at ribosomes

actinomycin D inhibits DNA synthesis

rifamycin inhibits RNA synthesis

polymixin B, amphotericin B and nystatin damage the cell membrane

Figure 62 *Some effects of antibiotic drugs on bacteria*

Table 11 *Some therapeutic antibiotics*

ANTIBIOTIC	SOURCE	ACTION SPECTRUM
Penicillin G	*Penicillium notatum*	antibacterial
Bacitracin	*Bacillus subtilis*	antibacterial
Polymixin	*Bacillus polymyxa*	antibacterial
Chloramphenicol	*Streptomyces venezuelae*	antibacterial
Amphotericin B	*Streptomyces nodosus*	antifungal
Actinomycin D	*Streptomyces parvullus*	antitumour

6.2 STEROIDS

Steroid-like substances from plants are converted into steroid hormone analogues by the action of micro-organisms. These laboratory made molecules, which resemble natural steroid hormones, are in considerable demand. They may be used as the principal ingredients of contraceptive pills, or for hormone replacement therapy. As almost equal demand exists for anti-inflammatory agents, used to treat autoimmune diseases, or to suppress the immune response after organ transplantation. Stigmasterol, from soya beans, can be used as the raw material for the synthesis of **prednisone** and **prednisolone**, anti-inflammatory drugs. Cell cultures from roots of the Mexican barbasco plant *(Dioscorea deltoidea)* are the source of a steroid called diosgenin. This is the raw material used to produce both **oestrogen** and **progesterone**. Typically, during fermentation, micro-organisms add a hydroxyl group to one of the 17 carbon atoms in the core of a steroid molecule, as in each of the following reaction steps:

$$\text{Corticosterone} \xrightarrow[\substack{\textit{Cunninghamella} \\ \textit{blakesleeana}}]{\text{Fermented by}}$$

$$\text{hydrocortisone} \xrightarrow[]{\substack{\text{Fermented by} \\ \textit{Mycobacterium} \\ \textit{globiforme}}} \text{prednisolone}$$

6.3 VACCINES

Vaccination has been used for many years to give immunity against specific contagious diseases. Vaccines are prepared from the surface proteins, **antigens**, of the agents responsible for the disease. A person may be vaccinated by injecting proteins from a dead organism (as is the case with whooping cough and diphtheria vaccines), or with bacterial toxins, which are chemically treated to reduce their virulence (for example tetanus vaccine). Alternatively, 'live' pathogens that have undergone 'attenuation', may be used. Attenuation is a series of induced mutations that destroy their virulence, yet leave some of their surface antigens intact. Poliomyelitis and measles vaccines are produced from attenuated strains.

Biotechnology offers a number of new approaches to vaccine production.

Hepatitis B
Hepatitis B is a viral disease of humans, causing malfunctions of the liver, and, in some cases, cancer of the liver. It was discovered that the blood serum from infected persons carried a surface antigen from the virus (HBsAg). The DNA which coded for this surface antigen was cloned in yeast cells. Large quantities of the surface antigen were subsequently produced by the yeasts. After purification, this antigen was found to be effective as a vaccine, raising antibodies that gave protection against the hepatitis B virus. (If a vaccine is prepared from a surface antigen, rather than an attenuated virus, there is no possibility that vaccination will ever cause disease. This occasionally happened when attenuated strains of

(a) *Hepatitis B vaccine*

surface antigens

Yeast cell

Hepatitis B virus

transfer viral DNA for surface antigens to yeast nucleus

yeast cell secretes viral surface antigens

purified viral antigen used as vaccine

(b) *Possible vaccine against malaria*

Vaccinia virus

malarial parasite

transfer gene for malarial parasite surface antigens to vaccinia virus

virus produces surface antigens of malarial parasite

purified antigen used as vaccine

Figure 63   Producing vaccines by genetic engineering

a virus, such as the poliomyelitis virus, recovered their virulence after injection into the bloodstream.)

Cowpox

Cowpox or **vaccinia virus** is of considerable interest because it is one of the largest viruses and will accept large amounts of extra DNA. By a complex procedure involving bacterial plasmids and *E. coli*, the virus has been engineered to incorporate and express foreign DNA from HIV (the AIDS virus), influenza, herpes and the malarial parasite. The protein products of this foreign DNA are expressed at the surface of the vaccinia virus. It is hoped that these surface antigens can be used as vaccines, to raise antibodies against those organisms from which the foreign DNA was taken.

With the introduction of unstirred airlift fermenters (p.55) large scale tissue culture has become available for medical and veterinary virus vaccine production. Bacterial cultures for use in vaccine production are grown in relatively small stainless steel fermenters, of 1000 dm^3 or less. The internal pressure within these fermenters is kept below atmospheric pressure, to reduce the risk of pathogenic bacteria being blown out into the atmosphere. Furthermore, the exhaust gases pass through a sterilising filter, or incinerator, or both so that there is effective containment.

6.4 MONOCLONAL ANTIBODIES

Antibodies are protective proteins produced by B-lymphocytes in response to foreign molecules, called **antigens**. These are mostly proteins, polysaccharides or other macromolecules. Each antibody is a Y-shaped protein, consisting of two light and two heavy chains, held together by sulphur bonds. The middle region is hinged, so that the angle between the two arms can be varied. At the tip of each arm is a binding region. Both binding regions on an antibody are specific for the same type of antigen (Figure 64a). Figure 64b shows how antibodies bind to antigens on the surface of a cell, such as a bacterium or tumour cell. There are many tens of thousands of different types of antibody, each binding a different type of antigen.

One important biological feature of an antibody is that it binds specifically to the antigen molecule that triggered its production. Within human tissues, antibodies bind only to a small part of their antigens, which are much larger molecules, thereby tagging them for destruction by the immune system. As the surfaces of viruses and cell walls of bacteria contain a large number of antigenic molecules, those viruses and bacteria that invade human tissues normally become tagged with many different antibodies.

In the early 1970s research into antibody function was thwarted by the problem that antibody-producing cells could not be maintained in culture for more than a few days. A solution came in 1975, following from the work of G. Kohler and G. Milstein. Their approach was to fuse the short-lived antibody-producing cells with cancer cells that live indefinitely. They injected mice with sheep red blood cells, which are highly antigenic. B-lymphocytes were then harvested from the spleens of the mice and fused with myeloma cells from bone marrow to form hybrids. After selection on appropriate semi-solid media, some clones of these cells specifically recognised sheep red blood cells. As all the members of the same clone produced the same antibody they were called **monoclonal antibodies**. The relatively simple production technique allowed specific monoclonal antibodies to be produced in response to any known antigen. As the role of an antibody is to seek out and tag a specific antigen, monoclonal antibodies hold the promise of acting like 'magic bullets', with the ability to find and destroy any foreign material in the tissues, from a pathogen to a cancer cell.

(a) *General structure*

(b) *Antibody-antigen binding*

Figure 64   Antibodies

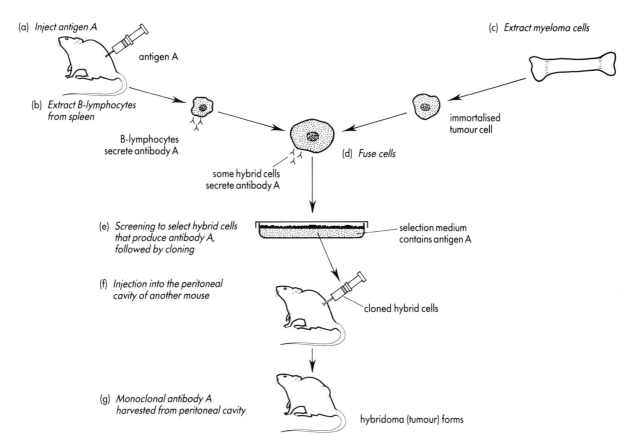

(a) *Inject antigen A*

antigen A

(b) *Extract B-lymphocytes from spleen*

B-lymphocytes secrete antibody A

some hybrid cells secrete antibody A

(c) *Extract myeloma cells*

immortalised tumour cell

(d) *Fuse cells*

(e) *Screening to select hybrid cells that produce antibody A, followed by cloning*

selection medium contains antigen A

(f) *Injection into the peritoneal cavity of another mouse*

cloned hybrid cells

(g) *Monoclonal antibody A harvested from peritoneal cavity*

hybridoma (tumour) forms

Figure 65   *General principles of monoclonal antibody production*

Clearly, specific or monoclonal antibodies have many uses, both in current clinical medicine and in medical research. Some of their more important applications are listed below:

(i) The ability to tag specific proteins with a marked antibody is an invaluable tool in biomedical research, because it enables researchers to follow the movements of a protein and so find out exactly what it does.

(ii) Monoclonal antibodies, labelled with a fluorescent dye or radioactive isotope, are used to identify the distribution of antigens, such as those of pathogens or cancer cells, in tissue sections.

(iii) Before organ transplantation is undertaken, tissues of the donor and recipient are tissue-typed. The better the match between cell surface proteins, the better the chances of success, with less tissue rejection. Monoclonal antibodies, raised in response to these cell surface protein, have allowed more accurate tissue-typing to be undertaken.

(iv) Patients who have undergone kidney transplants are currently treated with a monoclonal antibody called 'Orthoclone OKT-3'. This specifically reacts with OKT-3 antigen on the surface of T-lymphocytes, the cells that mount an attack on the 'foreign' kidney. It is claimed that this treatment has saved the kidneys of 90% of the patients whose bodies would have rejected them.

(v) Dipsticks, such as those used for pregnancy-testing, are impregnated with antibodies, some attached to coloured latex particles. The urine of pregnant women contains an additional component, namely human chorionic gonadotrophin (hCG), a product of the placenta. This hormone binds to coloured mobile antibodies at the base of the dipstick. As urine diffuses upwards, the antibody-hormone complexes travel with it, but are stopped about one-third of the way up by a row of immobilised antibodies that also bind hCG. The accumulation of coloured antibody-hormone complexes at this level results in the formation of a coloured band (usually blue), indicating that the woman is pregnant. Conversely, if the woman is not pregnant and has no hCG in her urine, the mobile antibodies travel further up the dipstick, until they bind to a second band of immobilised antibodies, capable of forming complexes with the mobile antibody. A blue band at this higher level indicates a negative result.

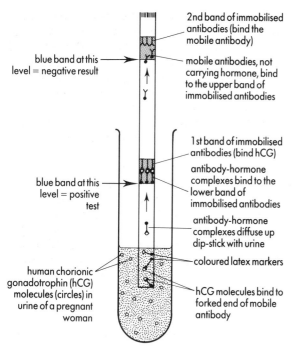

Figure 66 *Antibody-based dipstick for pregnancy testing*

Labels in figure:
- 2nd band of immobilised antibodies (bind the mobile antibody)
- blue band at this level = negative result
- mobile antibodies, not carrying hormone, bind to the upper band of immobilised antibodies
- 1st band of immobilised antibodies (bind hCG)
- blue band at this level = positive test
- antibody-hormone complexes bind to the lower band of immobilised antibodies
- antibody-hormone complexes diffuse up dip-stick with urine
- human chorionic gonadotrophin (hCG) molecules (circles) in urine of a pregnant woman
- coloured latex markers
- hCG molecules bind to forked end of mobile antibody

In the future, the applications of monoclonal antibodies may be broadened along any, or all, of the following lines:

(i) Combined with a powerful toxin, such as ricin, monoclonal antibodies could be targeted to bind to the surfaces of cancer cells, or pathogens such as viruses or bacteria. This site-specific release of toxins offers hope of destroying the foreign material without destroying surrounding healthy tissue.

(ii) Antibodies produced in response to drugs could be used to treat people who have taken an overdose. Blood of the overdosed person would be circulated outside the body, through a device containing monoclonal antibodies, which would remove the drug from the bloodstream.

(iii) Medically important substances, such as interferon, could be purified by using monoclonal antibodies to remove organic contaminants.

6.*5* TRANSGENIC ANIMALS

The production of medical products in transgenic animals – those that have had their genome altered by recombinant DNA technology (see section 8.1) – is an alternative to production by cell culture in fermenters.

Transgenic sheep and cattle have already been used to produce products of medical importance, such as interferon, blood-clotting factors and enzymes that dissolve blood clots. The biotechnology involved consists of transforming an animal by adding a gene for protein synthesis upstream of the gene that codes for milk production (Figure 67). Successful integration of the new gene results in secretion of the required protein in the animal's milk. Collecting the milk, and separating out the required protein, is a relatively simple process. An alternative approach is to harvest the required protein from the eggs of transgenic chickens. The chicken has a gene that codes for the production of large amounts of egg albumen. Replacing this gene with one that codes for a human protein could soon provide large amounts of novel proteins from eggs.

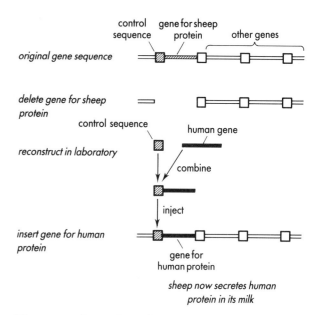

Figure 67 *Stages in replicating a gene for sheep protein, secreted into milk, with a gene for human protein*

Labels in figure:
- control sequence
- gene for sheep protein
- other genes
- original gene sequence
- delete gene for sheep protein
- control sequence
- human gene
- reconstruct in laboratory
- combine
- inject
- insert gene for human protein
- gene for human protein
- sheep now secretes human protein in its milk

The use of transgenic animals to produce drugs has a number of distinct advantages over the use of micro-organisms. These are:

(i) It is infinitely more cost-effective, as expensive culture-vessels for large-scale production, continuous monitoring of equipment, and maintenance are not required.

(ii) Animals such as sheep and cattle can add sugar residues to proteins. This makes them more effective and versatile synthesisers of desirable products than most micro-organisms.

(iii) Future demand for any product can be met by interbreeding transformed animals. The ability to secrete a required protein is passed from one generation to the next in accordance with Mendelian principles.

At the present time, however, there are problems in keeping transgenic animals alive. This means that the optimistic scenarios set out above are still some way off.

6.*6* GENE PROBES

Recombinant DNA technology has revolutionised the study of human single-gene disorders, such as sickle cell anaemia. The use of **gene probes**, which are short lengths of single-stranded DNA (or RNA) capable of binding to complementary single-stranded DNA segments, has allowed researchers to pinpoint the regions on chromosomes where the defective genes are located. Furthermore, gene probes have provided a specific test for single-gene disorders, applicable to embryos in the womb and to young children.

Sickle cell anaemia is caused by a mutation in a region of DNA that codes for the protein part of a haemoglobin molecule, the red pigment in blood. In the sickle celled condition, one of the bases in the DNA molecule, thymine, is replaced by adenine. That, in turn, leads to an amino acid sequence in which glutamate is replaced by valine. The resulting haemoglobin molecule (HbS) has a sticky patch on its surface and tends to form chains with other haemoglobin molecules. These distortions affect the shape of the red blood cells, which may become sickled, thereby losing some of their oxygen-carrying capacity, as well as becoming less efficient in releasing oxygen to the tissues. Affected individuals experience symptoms caused by the permanent destruction of their red blood cells, notably blocked vessels, anaemia and organ damage.

To identify a sickle cell carrier or sufferer, a purified DNA sample, usually extracted from white blood cells, is treated with the **restriction endonuclease M st II** (Figure 68). This enzyme cleaves the gene for normal haemoglobin (HbA) across the base sequence CCTGAGGAG. Cleavage takes place between the seventh (G) and eighth (A) bases in this sequence, generating a relatively short DNA fragment. The change of A → T in the gene for sickle cell haemoglobin (HbS) destroys the recognition site, or point at which the DNA is normally cut, thereby causing the enzyme to cut on either side of the mutation site. This means that the enzyme cuts the DNA of people with normal haemoglobin (HbA) and sickle cell haemoglobin (HbS) into fragments of different lengths. As Figure 68 indicates, the fragments from people with the sickle cell gene are slightly longer.

Figure 68   Stages in cutting DNA and preparing gene probes for identifying sufferers and carriers of sickle cell anaemia

Figure 69 shows all the procedures leading up to the identification of gene fragments with gene probes. The fragments are transferred to a well in a flat plate of agarose gel, contained in a box. Separation of the fragments by **electrophoresis** takes place when the apparatus is switched on. The fragments move through the gel at different rates, depending on their length. Small fragments travel faster than large ones. After several hours the fragments become arranged in parallel bands, each band containing many DNA fragments of uniform length. The pattern is then blotted onto a nitrocellulose filter. Heating binds the DNA to the filter and also separates each DNA fragment into its two single strands of DNA that contain complementary base sequences. Such binding is detected by placing an X-ray film over the nitrocellulose filter. When the film is developed, a radioactive region shows up as a dark band.

Gene probes are also used to detect the presence of DNA from pathogens, as in the diagnosis of AIDS and other viral conditions. In the future DNA probes may become available for the diagnosis of cancer. Cells become cancerous only after certain genes, called **oncogenes**, have been altered. Once altered, some cancerous cells produce a specific type of mRNA, not found in healthy cells. It should soon be possible to detect this mRNA by using a probe.

6.7 GENE THERAPY

A possible cure for single-gene disorders, such as sickle cell anaemia, lies in gene therapy. **Gene enhancement therapy** is an attempt to boost the effect of a gene that is generally thought to be desirable. Height, intelligence and athleticism are traits resulting from complex gene interactions. Once the individual genes that contribute to these attributes have been identified, attempts could be made to add additional copies to the genome. **Somatic gene replacement therapy** is an attempt to replace defective genes with normal ones. The technique, when it is developed, should be applicable to single-gene disorders in which homozygous recessive (aa) individuals show symptoms of the disease. Therapy would consist of adding normal genes to the genome, so that the recipient gains a normal gene, while retaining the defective ones (e.g. A + aa).

In an attempt to cure sickle cell anaemia, for example, the first stage of the laboratory some of these bone marrow cells would undergo genetic engineering. A single copy of the normal (HbA) gene would be inserted. Transformed cells would then be transferred to a suitable growth medium and allowed to multiply. At the appropriate time, the donor would receive radiation and drug

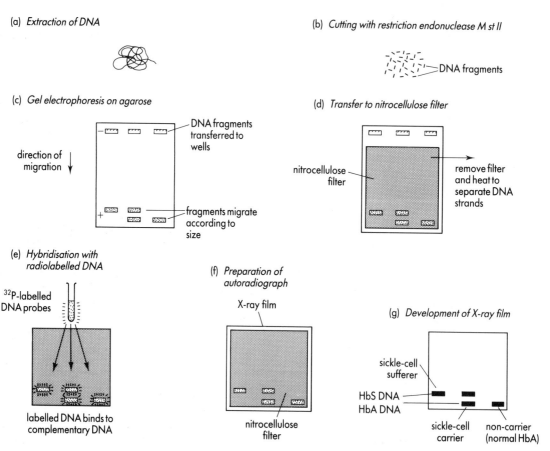

(a) *Extraction of DNA*

(b) *Cutting with restriction endonuclease M st II*

DNA fragments

(c) *Gel electrophoresis on agarose*

direction of migration

DNA fragments transferred to wells

fragments migrate according to size

(d) *Transfer to nitrocellulose filter*

nitrocellulose filter

remove filter and heat to separate DNA strands

(e) *Hybridisation with radiolabelled DNA*

32P-labelled DNA probes

labelled DNA binds to complementary DNA

(f) *Preparation of autoradiograph*

X-ray film

nitrocellulose filter

(g) *Development of X-ray film*

sickle-cell sufferer

HbS DNA
HbA DNA

sickle-cell carrier

non-carrier (normal HbA)

Figure 69 *Stages in detecting the sickle cell anaemia gene*

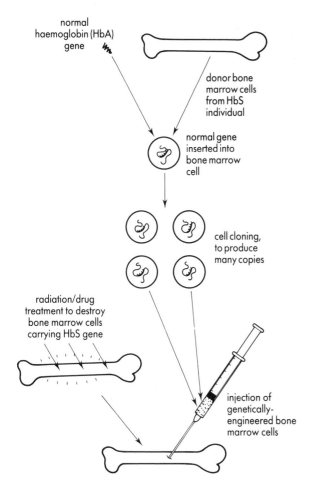

Figure 70   Possible gene therapy for sickle cell anaemia

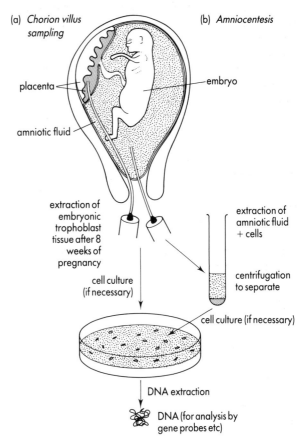

Figure 71   Methods of prenatal diagnosis for single gene disorders in human embryos

treatment to destroy his or her own bone marrow cells. These would be replaced by an injection of the donor's own genetically engineered bone marrow cells. Further treatment would ensure that the engineered cells continued to grow and multiply. At a point where the transplanted cells produced enough haemoglobin (HbA) to meet the individual's needs, a 'cure' would have been effected.

Two points should be noted in connection with gene replacement therapy. The first is that treated individuals continue to pass on defective genes in their sperm and eggs. In this case it is only the bone marrow cells, not other somatic cells or gametes, that contain the normal gene. The second point is that treated individuals carry three genes controlling globin synthesis (A + aa). Any harmful effects of this combination may take several years before they begin to show up.

A more distant aim of gene therapy is to effect a permanent cure for single gene disorders by inserting normal genes into sperm and eggs. This is **germ-line gene replacement therapy (eugenic gene therapy)**, a technique that would

enable a cure to be passed to the offspring of the treated individuals. At the present time, however, techniques are too imprecise to guarantee a predictable outcome.

6.8 GENETIC FINGERPRINTING

As we have seen, restriction endonucleases chop up DNA into fragments of different lengths. Careful analysis of the lengths of these fragments, following electrophoresis and other methods of separation, have shown that when restriction endonucleases act on a person's DNA, they chop it up into a unique collection of differently-sized fragments, from which the individual can be identified. This pattern is inherited.

This absolute specificity is the biological basis of **genetic fingerprinting**, a technique used in forensic science. It allows identifications of individuals from the lengths of their DNA fragments after samples of their DNA have been treated with restriction endonucleases. The DNA samples can be obtained from traces of blood, hair or semen, and so provides an invaluable diagnostic tool in crime detection. Furthermore, as some restriction fragments of exactly the same length are also found in an individual's nearest relatives (e.g. parents, children), the technique gives additional information about parentage pedigree. Animal breeders also use it to establish the pedigree of their stocks.

Throughout the human genome there are regions, called **hypervariable regions**, which show considerable variation in length from individual to individual. Further analysis of these hypervariable regions shows that they contain short sequences of DNA (e.g. GGAGGTGGGCAGGAG), now called **minisatellites**, that are repeated many times over. Individual differences in the lengths of restriction fragments appear to depend, in part, on the number of times each minisatellite is repeated within the hypervariable region.

Using the technique described in section 6.6, DNA fragments from the hypervariable region have been separated by electrophoresis and radiolabelled to produce a **genetic fingerprint**. A completed fingerprint (Figure 72), consisting of many parallel bars (rather like the bar code on groceries), was found to be unique to each individual. Moreover, when the genetic fingerprint of a child was compared with those of its parents, each band in the child's print was seen to derive directly either from its father or mother. This provided a method of establishing true blood relationships in cases of disputed parentage.

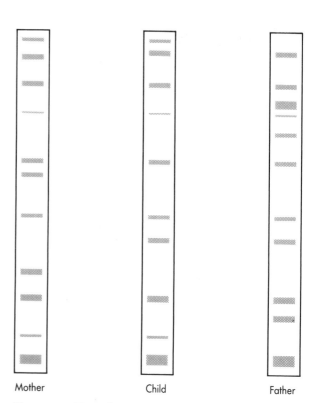

Mother   Child   Father

Figure 72   Hypothetical 'genetic fingerprints' of a child and its parents. Note that each individual has a unique print and that the child's print is derived from its mother and its father

The DNA fingerprinting technique, discovered in 1984, was used to determine the father of the above litter of Siberian huskies in order to register them with proof of pedigree

A blood smear from someone with sickle cell anaemia. Note the sickled appearance of some red blood cells

QUESTIONS

1 The diagram below shows the effects of four different antibiotics on the bacterium *Bacillus subtilis*.

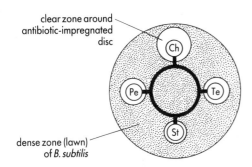

clear zone around antibiotic-impregnated disc

dense zone (lawn) of *B. subtilis*

a) Suggest names for the four antibiotics, each indicated by their first and second letters.
b) List the antibiotics in order of their potency.
c) Use the formula πr^2 to find the area of the clear zone around each disc ($\pi = 3.14$). By what numerical factor is
  (i) Ch more potent than Pe, and
  (ii) Te more potent that St?
d) Comment on the accuracy of the results.

2 The diagram below shows an agarose gel used in electrophoresis to separate fragments of DNA.

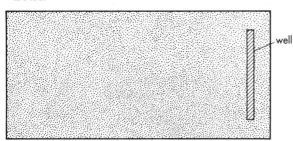

well

Copy the diagram.
a) Add an arrow to one side of your diagram to indicate the direction of electrophoresis.
b) On the opposite side of your diagram indicate the position of the anode (+) and (−).
c) Three double-stranded fragments of DNA are separated by a electrophoresis. Indicate on your diagram the relative positions of these strands after electrophoresis.
   TTAGC   ATCGGGC   AACCGTATTCG
   AATCG   TAGCCCG   TTGGCATAAGC
d) How is the double-stranded DNA fixed and separated?
e) Write out the base sequences of DNA probes that would bind to the longest DNA fragment.
f) How may binding between a DNA probe and its complementary DNA fragment be detected?

3 Distinguish between narrow-and broad-spectrum antibiotics.
Give an account of the discovery and subsequent large-scale production of an antibiotic such as penicillin.
Explain how penicillin, and other antibiotics, kill bacteria.

4 What is a vaccine?
Describe the effects of vaccination in terms of changes within the immune system. What new approaches to vaccine production are offered by biotechnology?

5 Describe the production, and therapeutic applications of
a) monoclonal antibodies
b) steroids
c) interferon
d) human insulin or growth hormone

6 Describe a gene probe and discuss how gene probes have been used in forensic medicine.
How would you use a gene probe to diagnose a disease such as sickle cell anaemia?

7 What is gene therapy?
Outline ways in which single gene defects might be treated by gene therapists.
Discuss the ethics of manipulating the human genome.

BIBLIOGRAPHY

Clinical and Forensic Medicine

Brown, CM and Duffas, JH (1984) Health impact of biotechnology *Swiss Biotechnology* (2) 7-32

Chang, TMS ed.(1977) *Biomedical Application of Immobilised Enzymes and Proteins* (vol 1 and 2) Plenum Press, New York

Hartley, BS, Atkinson, T and Lilley, MD eds (1983) *Industrial and Diagnostic Enzymes* The Royal Society, London

Rosazza, J P (1982) *Microbial Transformations of Bioactive Compounds* CRC Press, Florida

7 INDUSTRIAL CHEMICALS

Many commercially useful chemical compounds are produced by micro-organisms. The range is almost limitless. Those that are most widely manufactured, or used in industrial processes, fall within the broad categories of proteins, polysaccharides, fuels, solvents and organic acids. Micro-organisms are also widely used in oil and metal extraction . They serve either to enhance oil recovery or to increase the amount of metals, notably iron, copper and uranium, that can be recovered from ores.

7.1 PROTEINS

Enzymes are the most important group of commercial proteins, with a wide range of uses as therapeutic and catalytic agents. A large market also exists for three hormones: insulin, human growth hormone (HGH) and bovine growth hormone (BGH). Other human proteins with therapeutic potential are also in demand. These include those used to treat thrombosis (e.g. urokinase), respiratory disorders (e.g. lung surfactant protein) and tumours (e.g. interferon and interleukin–2).

7.1.1 Enzymes

The bulk of enzymes used commercially are obtained from microbial sources. Relatively few come from plants or animals. **Extracellular enzymes**, secreted by bacteria and fungi into their surroundings, are harvested by filtration and then concentrated. **Intracellular enzymes**, retained within cells, are released by breaking down cell walls and membranes with detergents, alkalis or lysozyme. After centrifuging and filtering off the debris, the enzymes can be 'salted out' by adding high concentrations of very soluble salts such as ammonium sulphate, sodium sulphate and phosphate buffers. The solubility of many enzymes at high salt concentrations decreases logarithmically as the salt concentration increases. Further purification involves precipitation in organic solvents such as methanol, ethanol and acetone. Large scale purification can be achieved by various chromatographic techniques. In **affinity chromatography**, for example, antibodies are raised against an enzyme by injecting it into an animal such as a rabbit. These antibodies are harvested, purified and attached to an appropriate chromatographic matrix. The required enzyme binds selectively to the antibody. Subsequent desorption, by changing the pH or adding a dissociating agent such as urea, releases the enzyme from its antibody.

Enzymes are in many ways ideal catalysts for industrial processes because they occupy little space, react with only one component in a given mixture, and have a high rate of activity. They are, on the other hand, expensive to purify and often unstable in the purified state. Furthermore, optimal activity can be achieved only within fairly narrow limits of temperature and pH.

Figure 73 shows how a catabolic (breaking down) enzyme is believed to operate. The essential role of the enzyme is to provide an active site where large molecules bind to a template of complementary shape. Here, as they bind and break away in rapid succession, each molecule is cleaved into two smaller fragments.

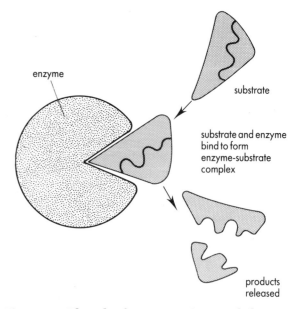

Figure 73   The role of an enzyme in a catabolic reaction

7.1.2 Uses of enzymes

The commercial applications of enzymes, already numerous, are increasing year by year. Table 12 lists some of these industrial, medical, analytical and manipulative applications. Some of the other applications are more complex, requiring an explanation.

Urea, for example, is a toxic compound that accumulates in the blood as a result of kidney failure. By using **microcapsules** containing urease, glutamate dehydrogenase and glucose dehydrogenase, possibly mixed with charcoal to absorb some of the ammonia, it may in future be possible to remove urea from the blood of a patient with kidney failure by use of enzymes (Figure 74a, page 82).

Enzymes are also one component of dip-sticks (Figure 74b, page 82) used by doctors for the rapid estimation of glucose, urea, ketones, cholesterol etc. in blood and urine. A small chemically-treated paper pad at one end of the stick changes colour if glucose or cholesterol, say, is present. The intensity of the colour indicates the approximate concentration of the solute. The pad usually contains an enzyme, which is specific for the substrate of interest, and peroxidase with a redox dye that changes colour when oxidised. The reaction takes place in two steps:

(i) $D\text{-glucose} + H_2O + O_2$
$$\downarrow \quad glucose\ oxidase$$
$H_2O_2 + D\text{–glucuronolactone}$

OR

$Cholesterol + H_2O + O_2$
$$\downarrow \quad cholesterol\ oxidase$$
$H_2O_2 + cholest\text{–}4\text{–}en\text{–}3\text{–}one$

(ii) $H_2O_2 + \text{reduced dye (coloured or colourless)}$
$$\downarrow \quad peroxidase$$
oxidised dye (coloured or differently coloured) $+ H_2O + \frac{1}{2}O_2$

In both medicine and the food industry there is an increasing demand for **amino acids**. Twenty amino acids are required to make human proteins, and nine are essential constituents of the diet, because we cannot make them ourselves. Many micro-organisms, however, can synthesise these essential amino acids. To date, enzymes from microbial sources have been used to produce lysine, an essential amino acid that is deficient in cereals. This product may provide a valuable food supplement for people living largely on

Table 12 **Some commercial applications of enzymes**

ENZYME	REACTION	APPLICATION
INDUSTRIAL Amylase	starch → glucose	glucose syrup for food industry 'biological' washing powders
Glucose isomerase	glucose → fructose	fructose syrup for food industry
Papain	proteins → peptones	tenderising meat
Proteases	proteins → peptones + amino acids	removal of 'haze' from beer (brewing) breakdown of gluten in flour (baking) coagulation of milk (cheesemaking) removal of hair from hides (leathermaking)
Pectinesterases	pectin → polygalacturonate + methanol	removal of 'haze' from beer
MEDICAL L–asparaginase	breakdown of L–asparagine	cancer chemotherapy (L–asparagine is needed for tumour growth)
Cholesterol oxidase	oxidation of cholesterol	estimation of cholesterol in blood
Glucose oxidase + peroxidase	oxidation of glucose	estimation of glucose in blood
Urokinase	plasminogen activation	removal of fibrin clots (after heart attacks)
ANALYTICAL Carbonic anhydrase	inactivation by some insecticides	detection of insecticides in drinking water
Cholinesterase	inactivaiton by some insecticides	detection of insecticides in drinking water
Urease	Urea → $CO_2 + NH_3$	estimation of urea in urine and blood
MANIPULATIVE Lysozyme	peptide hydrolysis	disrupts bacterial and yeast cell walls

(a) *Extracorporeal (outside body)
shunt for removing urea)*

(b) *Dip-stick*

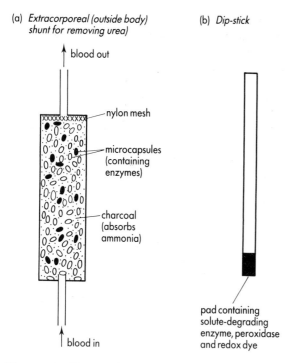

Figure 74   *Two medical applications of enzymes*

vegetables, enabling them to utilise more of the other amino acids present in their food.

7.1.3 Immobilisation of enzymes

Until quite recently, many enzyme-catalysed reactions were operated on a commercial scale by using enzyme/substrate/water mixture. This system led to enzymes being wasted. It was often difficult to remove enzymes from the end-products, and even more difficult to purify the recovered enzyme, so that it could be used again. An increasing demand for pure enzymes and their products led to **enzyme immobilisation**. This is a technique whereby an enzyme is bound immovably to a surface, and not allowed to mix with a solution of its substrate. Binding the enzyme to a solid support means that it cannot contaminate the end products of a reaction, and also that the same enzyme can be used over and over again. Furthermore, immobilisation enables some enzymes to retain their activity in high concentrations of organic solvents, including alcohol (ethanol). This is important in fuel alcohol production.

Enzyme immobilisation may be used to bind either the enzymes themselves, or cells capable of producing them. Three principal methods of immobilisation are currently in use.

   (i) **Adsorption**, or physical binding to a support such as glass beads, dextran microbeads or DEAE–cellulose. This process stems from physical rather than

chemical reactions. Charge effects and hydrophobic interactions may be involved.
  (ii) **Entrapment** within a gelatinous or fibrous polymer matrix of sodium alginate, polyacrylamide or collagen. The enzyme is trapped in a droplet of solvent, within a gelatinous polymer matrix.
 (iii) **Covalent bonding** to carboxymethylcellulose. The enzyme is tightly bound to its supporting system.

Immobilisation may affect the shape and properties of enzyme molecules. The enzyme substrate, for example, may not be bound so effectively, which causes the rate of reaction to fall. This disadvantage, however, may be offset by the fact that immobilisation may increase the temperature and pH range over which an enzyme remains active.

(a) *Adsorption*

The enzyme is held in position by interactions between oppositely charged particles

(b) *Entrapment*

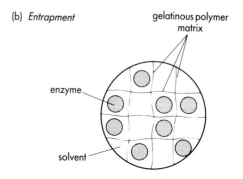

The enzyme is entrapped in a gelatinous matrix

(c) *Covalent bonding*

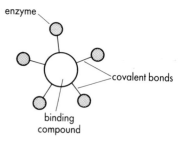

The enzyme is chemically bound to a supporting material

Figure 75   *Methods of enzyme immobilisation*

7.1.4 Enzyme-based biosensors

At present there is a lot of commercial interest in rapid biochemical analysis. Biosensors, for analysing biologically active compounds in solution, could simplify the work of doctors, the police and analytical chemists. If doctors obtained rapid estimates of glucose, urea and hormones in blood samples, they could make more rapid diagnoses, saving time on procedures that are currently carried out in hospital laboratories. Self-testing by the public for, say, glucose levels in urine, or blood pressure, could have important implications for preventative medicine. Biosensors would also be of value to the police. They could obtain rapid estimates of blood alcohol (ethanol) levels in drink-drive suspects, or rapidly identify a drug from blood samples of those who had overdosed. The work of analytical chemists would also be simplified if they could read off levels of nitrates, herbicides and phenols in water supplies.

Three main types of enzyme-based biosensors are currently in use or under development: enzyme transducer sensors, enzyme thermistors and biochips. A simple **enzyme transducer sensor**, or **enzyme electrode**, for measuring the amount of urea in blood or urine, is shown in Figure 76. Immobilised urease, surrounded by a membrane that is permeable to urea, is packed around the tip of an ammonium ion probe, When the probe is dipped into a solution containing urea, molecules of the solute diffuse through the membrane and are broken down into carbon dioxide and ammonium ions by the immobilised enzyme:

$$Urea + H_2O \rightarrow CO_2 + NH_4^+$$

The volume of ammonium ions released in a given time is proportional to the concentration of urea in the solution. An appropriate transducer converts levels of the ammonium ions into an electrical signal. This signal, after amplification, is displayed. The strength of the electric current is proportional to the concentration of urea.

An **enzyme thermistor** is a biosensor that measures minute changes in temperature during exothermic reactions. Such devices are sensitive to temperature changes between 0.004°C and 1.0°C, the amount of heat generated during a reaction being directly proportional to the concentration of the reactants. In these biosensors the thermistor is mounted at the centre of a well-insulated, immobilised enzyme column.

The miniaturisation of biosensors has led to the production of a **biochip**. In a biochip used to detect glucose, for example, a key component is immobilised glucose oxidase, which catalyses the reaction:

$$Glucose + O_2 + H_2O \rightarrow Gluconic\ acid + H_2O_2$$

This reaction generates acids, or more specifically positive charges (H^+) which collect in the immobilised enzyme at the upper surface of the insulating layer. Negatively charged electrons (e^-) from the silicon support are attracted to the positive charges. The flow of electrons, through the silicon terminals, generates a current which is proportional to the amount of glucose in solution.

(a) *The probe*

ammonium ion probe
rubber band
semipermeable membrane
urea
immobilised urease

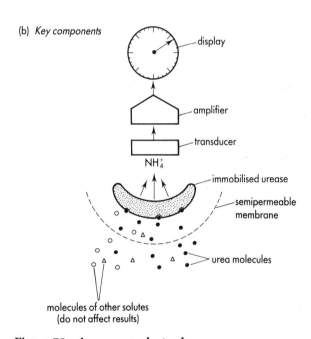

(b) *Key components*

display
amplifier
transducer
NH_4^+
immobilised urease
semipermeable membrane
urea molecules
molecules of other solutes (do not affect results)

Figure 76   An enzyme electrode

7.2 POLYSACCHARIDES

Some bacteria have a polysaccharide layer outside their cell wall. Aqueous suspensions of these **exopolysaccharides** have high viscosity. This viscosity falls as stress (pressure) is applied. Xanthan gum, synthesised by *Xanthomas campestris*, is used in the extraction of oil from wells. This compound, mixed with water, a surfactant and hydrocarbons, is pumped into the ground via an injection well. As it passes through rock pores this highly viscous polymer flushes out oil droplets. A water-gum-oil mixture collects at

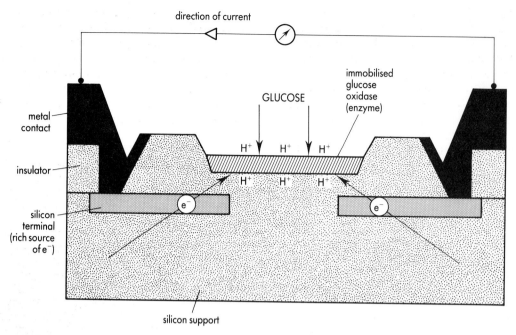

Figure 77   A glucose-sensitive biochip (sectional view). H$^+$ ions, generated by the reaction between glucose and glucose oxidase, attract electrons (e$^-$), thus creating a current

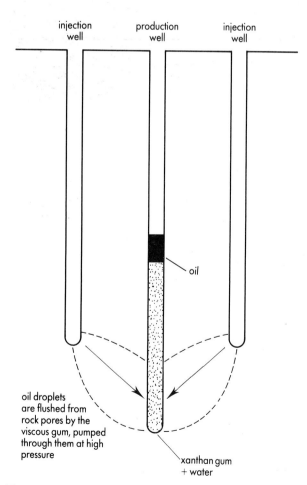

Figure 78   Oil extraction. Xanthan gum, driven down the injection wells, increased oil flow into the production well

the bottom of the production well. After pumping this mixture to the surface, oil separates out as a surface layer.

Emulsan, a polysaccharide from *Acinetobacter calcoaceticus*, mixed with a surfactant, is used to break up oilspills. The gum ensures that the surfactant remains in contact with the oil. Gelatinous dextrans, produced by *Leuconostoc mesenteroides*, are used as adsorbants and blood expanders. *Pseudomonas* is the source of gellan, a food gelatinising agent.

7.3 FUELS AND SOLVENTS

Using micro-organisms to produce fuels has many advantages. Cell fermentations operate at temperatures between 30–50°C, whereas coal- or oil-based fuel production processes require much higher temperatures, driven by burning fossil fuels. In addition to generating smoke, coal-and oil-based processes operate under conditions that may be extremely acid or alkaline. Furthermore, they may depend on expensive catalysts such as platinum. Biological processes don't pollute the atmosphere. They also operate at moderate pH and are driven by enzymes.

Ethanol (alcohol) is a solvent, an intermediate in the production of many chemical compounds and a fuel. As combustion engines can be driven on petroleum, ethanol, or a mixture of both, there is considerable interest in ethanol production in those countries that do not have their own oil reserves. As Figure 79, page 85, shows, it is possible to use lignocellulose, cellulose, starch and sugar as raw materials for ethanol production, but these must first be converted into glucose and fructose before they can be fermented by yeasts (*Saccharomyces sp.*). Bacteria of the genus *Zygomonas*, however, can make direct use of cellulose as a substrate in a sequence of reactions that also results in ethanol production. For this reason, and because *Zygomonas* can tolerate higher ethanol concentrations before its activity is inhibited, it is the most widely used organism in biological ethanol production.

During World War 1 there was considerable demand for **glycerol**, used as an ingredient in explosives. It was produced by adding bisulphite to the fermentation broth, when glucose was fermented by *Saccharomyces cerevisiae*. Dihydroxyacetone phosphate, and not acetaldehyde, was formed as an intermediate, with the consequent generation of glycerol in place of ethanol. Today, glycerol and some of its derivatives are used as anti-freeze agents. In some countries glycerol is being produced by the unicellular green alga *Dunaliella bardawil*, a holophyte, which converts solar energy directly into glycerol. The normal function of glycerol in this organism is to counteract the high osmotic pressure created by high salinity in its natural environment.

Acetone, produced by the fermentation of starch by the aerobic bacterium *Clostridium acetobutylicum*, is important in the manufacture of explosives used to propel heavy artillery shells. **Butanol**, a second product of the same fermentation process, is used in the manufacture of brake fluid, resins and plasticisers. A third product of the reaction is **hydrogen**. Interest in this product is increasing, mainly as a result of its use as rocket fuel, and in the production of electricity. It seems very probable that photosynthetic bacteria will be utilised as the future producers of this gas.

Ethanol – containing petrol

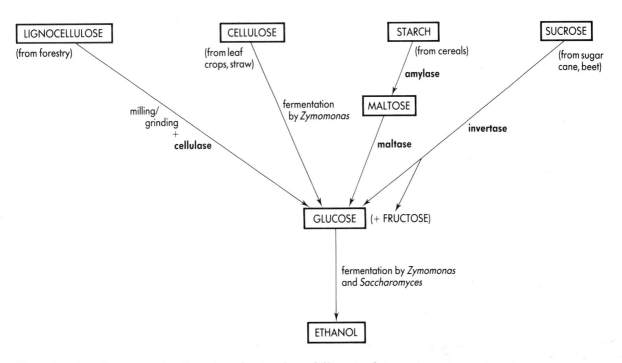

Figure 79   Possible routes to ethanol production from different substances

7.4 ORGANIC ACIDS

Acetic (ethanoic) acid is the most important organic acid, used in the manufacture of rubber, plastics, fibres and insecticides. Strains of *Acetobacterium* and *Clostridium* are capable of converting cellulose into acetic acid.

Lactic acid is used in the food processing industry, in tanning and for making plastics. It is produced from starchy material, treated with amylases, then fermented by *Lactobacillus bulgaricus* and closely related species.

Citric acid is used in the manufacture of soft drinks, confectionery and foods, where it acts both as a flavouring and antioxidant, preventing the breakdown of vitamin C. The acid is also used as a cleaning and descaling agent. Sodium citrate replaces phosphates in some detergents. Zinc citrate is added to toothpaste, where it prevents the formation of dental plaque. The mould fungus *Aspergillus niger* is used in the manufacture of citric acid. Molasses is the usual substrate. The fungus is grown either in open trays, or in a fermenter. Slaked lime is added to the end product to precipitate citric acid as calcium citrate. The acid is freed by adding sulphuric acid, then purified by using activated carbon and ion exchange resins.

Several other organic acids, including malic, tartaric, salicylic, succinic and pyruvic, can be made by biological processes. At the present time their industrial uses are somewhat limited but likely to increase in the future.

7.5 PLASTICS

Plastics produced from oil-based products are not biodegradable. The only way in which they can be destroyed is by burning. Many bacteria, including *Alcaligenes eutrophus*, *Azotobacter beijerinckii* and *Bacillus megaterium*, store a thermoplastic polyester called poly–B–hydroxybutyrate (PHB), as granules, in their cytoplasm. This material, after extraction with chloroform and methanol, yields a plastic which is biodegradable under anaerobic conditions. After scientists have found ways of producing this plastic in large quantities it will, no doubt, find many applications.

7.6 METAL EXTRACTION

Micro-organisms are used in the extraction of iron, copper, zinc and uranium from their ores. The technique is to make a massive pile of mineral-bearing ore, sometimes as high as 300 metres. These so-called **leach dumps** are sprayed with a dilute solution of sulphuric acid at pH 1.5–3.0, which creates a favourable environment for bacteria, which is found in natural association with the ore, to leach out valuable mineral salts. One of the most important of these bacteria is *Thiobacillus ferrooxidans*, a chemoautotrophic species that obtains its energy from the oxidation of ferrous iron (Fe^{2+}) to ferric iron (Fe^{3+}) and from the oxidation of reduced forms of sulphur to sulphuric acid. This bacterium causes either the direct oxidation of sulphides to sulphates, or produces sulphates by a less direct route:

(i) $MS + 2O_2 \rightarrow MSO_4$ (general equation, in which M = metal)

(ii) $4FeS_2 + 15O_2 + 2H_2O \rightarrow 2Fe_2(SO_4)_3 + 2H_2SO_4$

(iii) $2CuS + 2Fe_2(SO_4)_3 \rightarrow 2CuSO_4 + 4FeSO_4 + 2S$

When copper is mined, leach solutions, emerging from the bottom of the leach dumps, are retained in leach basins. Iron is then added to precipitate copper e.g.

$$CuSO_4 + Fe \rightarrow Cu + FeSO_4$$

The copper is further purified by smelting. Attempts are currently under way to produce genetically engineered strains of *T. ferrooxidans* that show faster reaction rates, greater tolerance to acid and saline conditions, and increased tolerance of toxic metal ions.

In the future, bacteria and fungi may be used to recover metals from solution. Negatively charged molecules in the cell walls of these micro-organisms bind and retain positively charged metal ions. This process, called '**biosorption**', is readily reversed when acids are added. With further development the process could be used to remove heavy metal ions (e.g. Hg, Pb, Cu, Cd, Zn) from toxic wastes, or to recover precious metals from their ores.

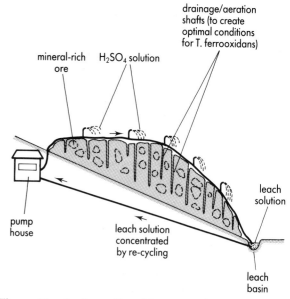

Figure 80   A mineral leaching operation

QUESTIONS

1 The graph below shows the relationship between temperature and the activity of two proteolytic enzymes, trypsin and papain.

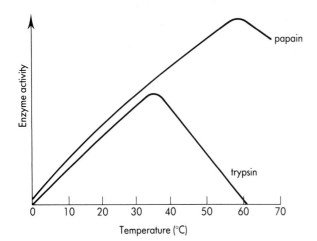

a) Name suitable sources of (i) trypsin and (ii) papain.
b) By reference to the graph explain why the activity of trypsin
  (i) increases over the temperature range 0–35°C, and
  (ii) falls over the temperature range 40–60°C.
c) What is the optimal temperature for the activity of (i) trypsin and (ii) papain?
d) In what way does the activity of papain differ from that of trypsin?
e) How do you account for this difference?
f) Explain why papain is of particular interest to biotechnologists.
g) Give a brief account of two commercial applications of papain.

2 Each of the following terms may be used in descriptive accounts of enzymes. What do you understand by each term?
a) Catalysis
b) Active site
c) Allostearic site
d) Turnover number
e) Denaturation
f) Specificity
g) Immobilisation
h) Oxidoreductase

3 Name four commercial sources of enzymes. How are raw enzymes a) extracted and b) purified?
Describe how enzymes are being used in a) medicine, b) the food industry and c) agriculture.

4 The development of enzyme immobilisation techniques since the 1950s has led to a boom in the industrial uses of enzymes.
Describe techniques for immobilising enzymes, and the industrial uses of enzymes in an immobilised form.

5 What are biosensors and how do they work? Describe and discuss ways in which biosensors are being used in medicine, industry and agriculture.

6 Natural fuel resources will eventually run out. Discuss the use of micro-organisms as producers of fuel for the future.
What advantages and disadvantages do you foresee in microbial fuel production?
Outline biochemical pathways by which starch, cellulose and hemicellulose might be converted into ethanol (alcohol).

7 Write notes on each of the following:
a) Microbial proteins and polysaccharides
b) Microbes and oil extraction
c) Microbes and metal extraction

BIBLIOGRAPHY

Industrial Chemicals

Bickerstaff, GF (1987) *Enzymes in Industry and Medicine* (New Studies in Biology) Hodder and Stoughton

Birch, GG, Blakebrough, N and Parker, KJ eds. (1981) *Enzymes and Food Processing* Applied Science Publishers, London

Carr, PW and Bowers, LD (1980) *Immobilized Enzymes in Analytical and Clinical Chemistry* John Wiley and Sons, New York and London

Gacesa, P and Hubble, J (1987) *Enzyme Technology* Open University Press, Milton Keynes

Goldstein, IS (1981) *Organic Chemicals from Biomass* CRC Press, Florida

Hacking, AJ (1986) *Economic Aspects of Biotechnology* Cambridge University Press, Cambridge

Rothman, H, Greenshields, RN and Calle, FR (1983) *The Alcohol Economy: Fuel Ethanol and the Brazilian Experience* Frances Pinter, London

Trevan, MD (1980) *Immobilised Enzymes* John Wiley and Sons, New York and London

Wynn, CH (1985) *The Structure and Function of Enzymes* (2nd edition) (Studies in Biology, No.42) Edward Arnold, London

AGRICULTURE AND HORTICULTURE

In the past, conventional breeding techniques have been used to improve farm animals, crop and ornamental plants. By selecting individuals with desirable traits, and crossing them so that there is sexual exchange and reshuffling of genes, breeders have produced offspring in which desirable traits have been combined. This method has been very successful in producing new varieties, but is often laborious and time consuming. In addition, recombination does not always separate tightly linked genes so that undesirable traits may appear alongside the desirable ones.

Biotechnology offers techniques that can break through the rules which limit variations achieved by sexual crossing. Genetic engineers can now transfer useful genes into farm stock, to improve their growth rates, milk or meat production. Although genetic engineering in plants has lagged behind, there are now several different techniques for improving yields from crop plants, and other procedures that increase plant variation. Micropropagation, widely used by horticulturists, provides a rapid method for obtaining large numbers of genetically identical plants.

8.1 TRANSGENIC FARM ANIMALS

A transgenic animal is an individual in which a gene (or genes) from another individual has been artificially inserted. In most of these animals the new genetic information forms a permanent part of the genome, and is passed on to their offspring according to the normal rules of Mendelian inheritance. So far, transgenic cattle, sheep, pigs, rabbits and chickens have been produced.

Figure 81 shows stages in the development of a mammalian embryo during its first six days of life. Immediately after a sperm has penetrated an egg genes from the male and female gametes are present in two small structures known as pronuclei. After the pronuclei have fused, the cell starts dividing. Successive mitotic divisions cleave the cell into 2, 4, 8, 16 and 32 – celled stages, transforming it into a solid ball of cells called a morula. This morula is surrounded by a

clear gelatinous outer covering, the zona pellucida. By the end of the fifth day, further cell divisions and cell movements, have transformed the developing embryo into a hollow, fluid-filled ball, called a blastocyst. The blastocyst's outer flattened layer of cells is its trophectoderm, from which the placenta forms. Its inner cell mass will go on to form the embryo proper. Implantation begins when the blastocyst sticks to the uterine wall and produces villi that anchor it into position (Figure 81).

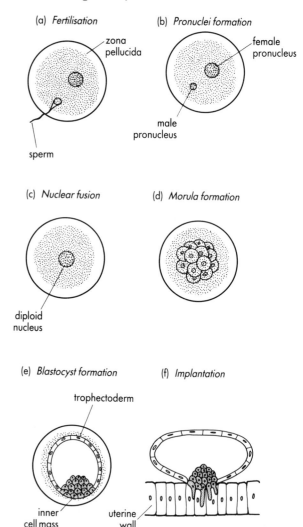

Figure 81   Stages in the early development of a mammalian embryo

Working with these early mammalian embryos, genetic engineers have used three different methods for introducing foreign genes:

(i) Injection of genes – sequences of DNA – into a pronucleus.

This is called microinjection. A fertilised egg is held, by suction, in a pipette. Several hundred copies of the foreign gene are injected into one of the pronuclei via a micropipette. This method is the most widely used and has, to date, proved the most successful. Even so, 30% of treated embryos degenerate and die within a few hours.

(ii) The use of retroviruses as vectors to carry foreign DNA into morulas.

After removing the zona pellucida, which viruses cannot penetrate, a morula is placed on a culture of fibroblasts infected with retroviruses. The retrovirus, genetically engineered to carry foreign DNA, infect cells of the morula as they are shed from the fibroblasts. This technique, however, often creates 'mosaic' offspring, where some cells contain the foreign gene, while others do not. The method also has limitations because the modified virus cannot leave the transgenic species. Under certain conditions it could mutate, regaining its ability to cause disease in the tissues where it occurs.

(iii) Retroviral infection of stem cells, which are then injected into the cavity of another blastocyst.

Stem cells, from the inner cell mass of an embryo, are infected with genetically-engineered retroviruses, then injected into the central cavity of a different blastocyst. The injected cells colonise the new embryo and participate in the formation of all the tissues, including the ovaries and testes from which cells are formed. So far, researchers have successfully used this technique for producing transgenic mice and hamsters. In the future they hope to develop the technique so that it can be used with farm animals.

Early research into the production of transgenic animals revealed a simple method for producing hybrids, called **chimeras,** between closely related species. Sheep-goat chimeras were produced by mixing four-celled sheep embryos with eight-celled goat embryos. After removing the zona pellucida from each egg, pressing the eggs together and incubating at 37°C, the cells reorganised and went on to form hybrid blastocysts. These blastocysts were then transferred to sheep foster mothers, where they continued their growth and development until the

(a) *Microinjection*

(b) *Viral infection*

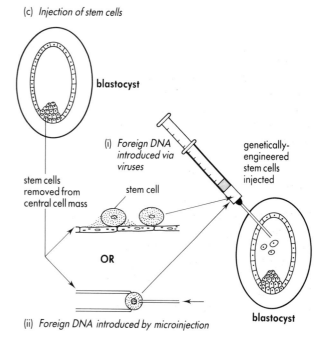
(c) *Injection of stem cells*

Figure 82   *Methods used to introduce foreign DNA into mammalian embryos*

sheep gave birth. Each hybrid offspring contained both sheep and goat cells in all its tissues. As a result, the coats of these animals resembled patchwork, made up from small irregular patches of sheep and goat fur. Although the chimeras proved to be of considerable academic and popular interest, combining features of the two species, they have, to date, had little economic significance.

The first transgenic animals produced were mice, into which a gene cloning for rat growth hormone was inserted by microinjection. Interestingly, the gene for growth hormone was linked to the promoter from a gene which responded to the presence of heavy metals. This acted as an unusual control mechanism, allowing the gene to be turned on by exogenous compounds, such as zinc. After extracting the appropriate DNA segment from a rat, it was

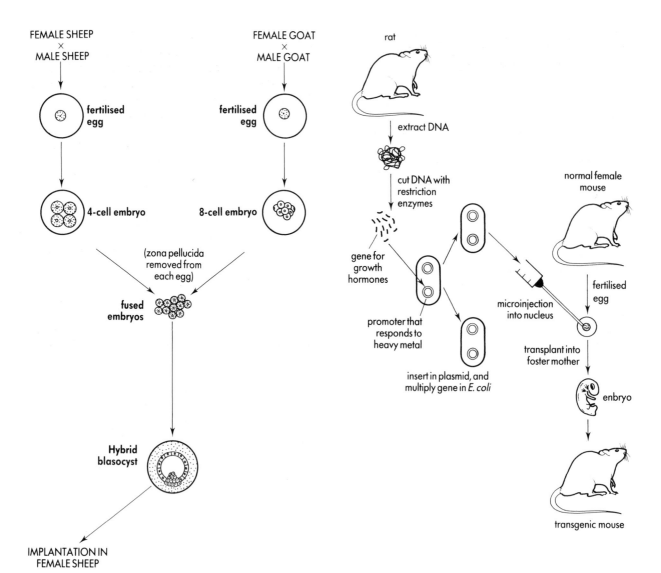

FEMALE SHEEP
×
MALE SHEEP

FEMALE GOAT
×
MALE GOAT

rat

fertilised egg

fertilised egg

extract DNA

cut DNA with restriction enzymes

4-cell embryo

8-cell embryo

normal female mouse

(zona pellucida removed from each egg)

gene for growth hormones

microinjection into nucleus

fertilised egg

fused embryos

promoter that responds to heavy metal

transplant into foster mother

insert in plasmid, and multiply gene in *E. coli*

enbryo

Hybrid blasocyst

transgenic mouse

IMPLANTATION IN FEMALE SHEEP

Figure 83   Stages in producing a sheep-goat chimera

Figure 84   Stages in producing a transgenic mouse

cloned in a plasmid and grown up in a standard laboratory culture of *E. coli* (Figure 84). The plasmids were then extracted, purified and converted to a linear form by adding the appropriate restriction endonucleases. Two techniques were used to introduce the new gene into the mouse genome:

(i)   As many as 10000 copies of the rat gene were injected into a pronucleus of a fertilised mouse egg, using a microneedle.

(ii) After treatment with calcium chloride, to make them more permeable, the rat DNA was applied to the outside of a 2–8–celled mouse embryo in culture.

The treated eggs, or embryos were then transplanted into foster mothers, where they continued their development. Embryos which has taken up the new gene were identified by DNA hybridisation with small samples of DNA from white blood cells or skin cells.

Transformed adult mice produced the growth

hormone mainly in their livers, rather than its normal site of synthesis in the pituitary. When fully grown, the body mass of these animals was about twice that of normal mice. They grew faster than the normal mice and converted their food more efficiently into body mass. Furthermore, their growth rate could be carefully controlled by altering the zinc content of their diet, a neat and simple method of control. From a practical viewpoint, interest is not so much in producing giant animals as in strains that reach marketable size faster and are more efficient in converting food into biomass. The transfer of other genes, such as those affecting the properties of hair, hides, cold-tolerance, disease-resistance and milk production might also produce strains of farm animals with economic advantages over existing stocks.

An account of the role of transgenic animals in the production of pharmaceutical products is given in section 6.5.

8.2 NEW BREEDING TECHNIQUES

In the future the quality of farm animals may be improved by two laboratory-based breeding techniques, notably embryo manipulation and embryo cloning.

Embryo manipulation has made it possible for farmers to increase their farmstock by novel methods. Female sheep and cattle produce, on average, one offspring per pregnancy. Twins are rare. The relatively simple technique of bisecting the fertilised egg at the two-celled stage, and transplanting each half into different regions of the uterus, has almost doubled the reproductive rate. Among treated animals **twin births** become the rule, not the exception. The technique of **embryo surgery,** used to produce twin births, is currently being extended to help conserve rare breeds. After fertilising their eggs in the laboratory, the young embryos of rare animals are dissected into anything from 2–8 cells. Each cell, successfully transplanted into a **surrogate mother** of a common breed, grows to produce a new individual of the rare type. Another variation of the technique allows surrogate mothers to carry embryos of a different species. Horses, for example, can give birth to zebras, from zebra embryos implanted at the blastocyst stage. The horse is tricked into accepting the zebra embryo by exchanging its own outer layer of trophectoderm for that of a horse embryo. This exchange doesn't affect development of the inner cell mass, the true embryo-forming region.

Embryo cloning is a technique that allows many genetically identical copies of an animal to be produced. Imagine that a mutation occurred in a cow making her an exceptional milk producer, significantly better than other members of her strain. Cross-breeding her with a bull would reshuffle her genes, and result in the loss of her unique characteristics. **Cloning**, to produce identical copies of the cow, is the only technique that will conserve her unique features for future generations.

Although it may be some years before the cloning of cattle becomes a common practice, success with mice shows the feasibility of techniques that are currently being used. An egg from the donor is grown in the laboratory to the blastocyst stage, then dissected to remove the inner cell mass. The mass is separated out into individual cells. A nucleus from each of these cells is injected into a one-celled embryo containing two pronuclei. After removing the pronuclei, the embryos are cultured in the laboratory until they reach the blastocyst stage. They are then transplanted into surrogate mothers.

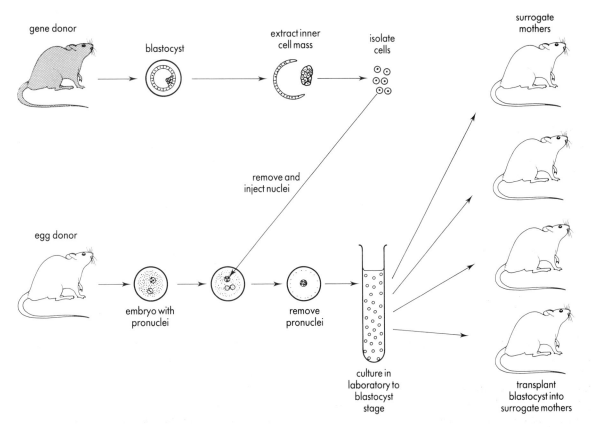

Figure 85   Stages in cloning the black mouse

8.3 MORE MILK WITH BST

Bovine somatotrophin (BST), also called growth hormone, is a natural protein hormone produced by a cow's pituitary gland. The hormone has three different physiological effects:

(i) It stimulates growth.

(ii) It affects the balance between fat and carbohydrate metabolism.

(iii) It increases milk production, partly by boosting food intake, but also by diverting a larger proportion of the cow's food into milk production.

During the 1970s, genetic engineers inserted the gene for BST into bacteria. As a result, large amounts of BST became available. Injected into cows it was found to increase milk production by anything from 25–40 per cent. The meat from treated cattle was leaner, making it more attractive to the consumer. By contrast, treated cows often became infertile, failing to respond to artificial insemination, or losing their embryos through spontaneous abortion. Widespread use of the product, and its subsequent appearance in milk and meat, led to public concern about its possible long-term effects on human health. Although research showed that BST was broken down in the human gut, and was physiologically active only in cattle, many people continued to have reservations about its use, not least because it seemed a somewhat cruel way of extracting milk from cows.

Table 13   Some advantages and disadvantages of using bovine somatotrophin (BST)

ADVANTAGES	DISADVANTAGES
Increased milk yields	cows eat more cows loose fertility
Higher profits for farmers	greater risk of mastitis and other bovine diseases
	milk overproduction
	fall in milk prices
	possible adverse effects on human health
	possibly a cruel and inhumane practice

8.4 TRANSGENIC PLANTS

Transgenic plants like their animal counterparts, are genetically engineered varieties containing one or more artificially inserted genes. The broad aim of carrying out such transformations is to improve crop yields, increase variety, and give cultivated plants more protection against their pests, parasites and harsh environmental conditions. Biologists first created transgenic plants by exploiting the bacterium *Agrobacterium tumefaciens.* This bacterium, the cause of crown gall disease, carries tumour-inducing (Ti) plasmids. One region of the plasmid, the so-called T–DNA region, integrates into any one of the plant's chromosomes. From its position on the chromosome, one part of the T–DNA codes for enzymes that synthesise the plant growth hormones auxin and cytokinin. Additional amounts of these hormones cause rapid cell division, resulting in the formation of a tumour.

Genetic engineers have exploited the discovery that any piece of foreign DNA, inserted between the left and right borders of the plasmid's T–DNA region is transferred to one of the plant's chromosomes, where it also becomes integrated. Since it was first discovered, this natural system for DNA transfer into plants has been improved in a number of ways. The genes that made the cells produce more hormones were deleted. As a result, transformed cells no longer grew into tumours, but retained their natural characteristics. Next, a gene from antibiotic resistance was added between the borders of the T–DNA region. Thirdly, sticky-ends were attached , so that the foreign DNA could be inserted.

After inserting the desired gene into a Ti plasmid, the remaining stages in producing a transgenic plant are fairly straightforward. Naked plant cells, or protoplasts, from which the cell walls have been removed, are placed into a petri dish and covered by a nutrient solution. A culture of *A.tumefaciens,* containing genetically-engineered plasmids, is added. The mixture is incubated at 25–30°C for several days. Cells are then plated out on to nutrient agar, to which appropriate antibiotic has been added. Only those plant cells that have taken up the gene for antibiotic-resistance – and with it the foreign DNA – will grow on this medium. After allowing several days for growth, living cells are harvested. Each cell may then be grown on to produce a complete plant by cultivation on nutrient media containing different mixtures of plant hormones.

Genetic variation in flowering plants can also be increased by methods that do not involve bacterial vectors. The flowering plants are all diploid (2n). In a majority of cases, sexual reproduction is species-specific and follows fertilisation of a haploid egg or ovum (n) by a haploid male gamete (n), formed in a germinating pollen grain. Haploid plants (n) can sometimes be formed by allowing pollen grains or anthers to grow on solid or in liquid cultures, to which an appropriate mixture of nutrients and growth hormones has been added. The plantlets

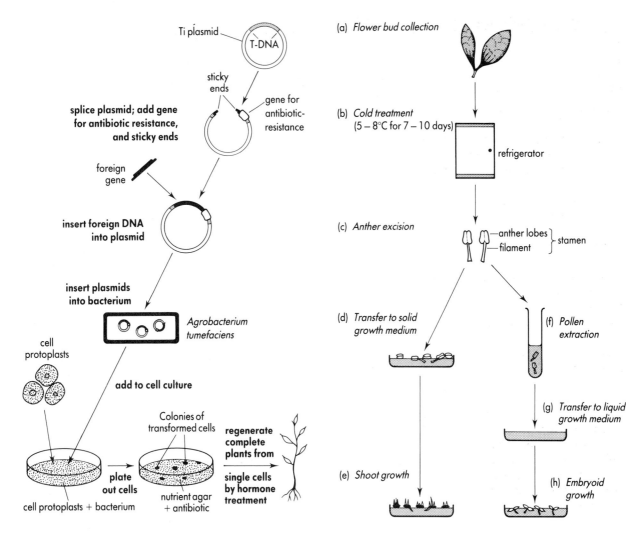

Figure 86   Using Agrobacterium tumefaciens *to produce transgenic plants*

Figure 87   Stages in anther and pollen cultivation

produced by pollen and anther culture are haploid, with only one copy of each gene. They often resemble their diploid parents, but may also show significant variation. By using colchicine, a mutagen which causes chromosome numbers to double during cell division, polyploid plants can be obtained with entirely new homozygous characteristics. This technique has been used to produce pure-breeding lines in less than half the time taken by conventional cross-breeding methods.

Protoplast fusion provides an additional technique for inducing variation in plant crops. A protoplast is the living part of a plant cell, surrounded by the cell membrane, from which the cell wall has been removed. By fusing protoplasts from different strains of species, it is possible to transfer genes from one strain to another. The protoplasts are prepared by immersing sterilised plant material in a solution of the enzyme cellulase, either from fungi or the alimentary canal of snails.

Protoplast fusion between varieties of a species, or closely related species, is achieved by adding ethylene glycol, or by applying an electric field. The technique has been successful in transferring genes for resistance to late blight fungus from one variety of potato to others. Only limited success, however, is reported in attempts to transfer genes for salt tolerance and disease-resistance from wild rice into cultivated varieties. Effective transfer occurred, but hybrids were difficult to identify and to grow on into mature plants. Research into protoplast fusion is continuing, with a view to finding new approaches to overcome these difficulties, enabling this technique to become a powerful tool in generating novel variations in plants.

8.4.1 Cereals

Cereals are among the world's most important food crops. In nature, *A. tumefaciens* (see section 3.3.2) does not attack cereals and so cannot be

(a) *Removal of lower epidermis from leaves*

forceps

leaf of strain A

leaf of strain B

(b) *Sterilisation*

sodium hypochlorite solution

(c) *Enzyme digestion of cell walls*

cellulase solution

(d) *Mixed protoplasts*

electrical or chemical treatment

(e) *Fusion*

fused protoplasts

Figure 88 **Stages in protoplast production and fusion**

Anther callus with shoots

used to modify the genome of these plants. If, however, the DNA of wheat dwarf virus is inserted into a Ti plasmid, bacteria carrying this plasmid will attack wounded wheat plants. Similarly, bacteria carrying Ti plasmids with DNA from maize streak virus will attack wounded maize plants. The technique, first used in 1987, is called **agroinfection**. Mature cereal plants are infected with plasmid-carrying bacteria. Transformed cells develop symptoms of the viral disease, and do not therefore need to be identified by selection. The infection spreads from cell to cell until all the cells of the cereal plant have been transformed. Researchers hope they will soon be able to use this technique for introducing foreign DNA into cereals.

Several other novel methods of gene transfer have been applied to cereals, all relying on the direct uptake of DNA without the use of a bacterial vector. In a technique called **electroporation**, plant protoplasts are mixed with foreign DNA and given an electric shock. The electric pulse causes pores to open up in the cell membranes, increasing the amount of exogenous DNA that enters. After the current is switched off the pores reseal. A small amount of the foreign DNA becomes incorporated into the chromosomes, causing some of the protoplasts to

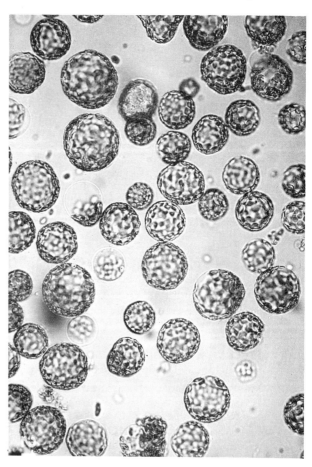

Leaf cell protoplasts

undergo transformation. So far, however, this technique has only been used successfully with maize and rice protoplasts. Similar results have been obtained by treating protoplasts with the chemical ethylene glycol, which makes them more permeable to exogenous DNA.

Attempts to transfer foreign DNA into wheat have mostly focused on young embryos. Results obtained from the direct **microinjection** of foreign DNA into young embryos have been mixed, with some transformations reported. Another similar method, **macroinjection,** involves the use of a syringe to inject foreign DNA into the space surrounding a young inflorescence. Success for this approach has been claimed in the transfer of a gene for resistance to the antibiotic kanamycin. Alternative approaches have included surrounding pollen grains, young carpels and mature seeds with exogenous DNA in the hope that they will take it up and undergo transformations. A different, novel and more promising approach involves the **bombardment** of intact plant cells with very small (1-4 μm in diameter) DNA-coated spheres of tungsten or gold. These microprojectiles are shot from a macroprojectile, resembling a bullet with an open tip, which is itself held by a stopping plate. The propulsive force which gives the microprojectiles sufficient acceleration comes either from a shotgun 'explosion' or an electrical discharge. Already successfully used in transforming soya beans, this approach could open a new chapter in the transformation of cereals.

Clearly the number of transformations that could be made in cereals is legion. Transferring *nif*-genes from legumes, so that cereals could fix atmospheric nitrogen, ranks high on the list of priorities. If cereals became self-sufficient in obtaining all their nitrogen, this would reduce the need for artificial fertilisers, and ease the problem of river pollution by nitrates. Rice growers might gain similar financial benefits if genes for salt-tolerance could be transferred into rice from one of the salt marsh grasses, or some other halophyte. Other transformations that might usefully be applied to cereals are equally applicable to other crops. Most consist of giving the crop plant better protection against its pests and parasites, while making it more resistant to harsh environmental conditions.

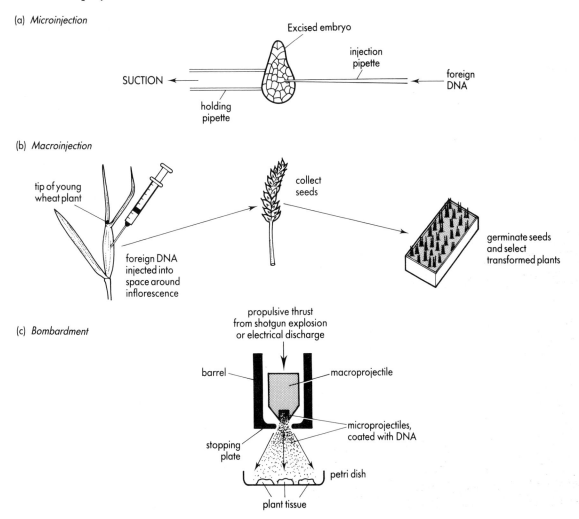

Figure 89   Methods used to introduce foreign DNA into cereals

8.5 CROP PROTECTION

Herbivorous insects are the greatest scourge of food crops, causing damage estimated at about £1.5 billion a year worldwide. One approach is to introduce micro-organisms into an area plagued by insects. *Baculovirus*, for example, is used to control spruce sawfly in coniferous forests. The fungus *Beauvaria bassiana* is effective in controlling aphids and the Colorado beetle on potatoes. *Bacillus thuringiensis*, a bacterium, is parasitic in the larvae of certain butterflies and moths. When the bacterium sporulates it produces a crystalline protein that kills the caterpillars. Sprayed over crops as a mixture of the bacterium and its crystalline toxin, this preparation has been effective in the control of inchworms and gypsy moth caterpillars. The toxin is commercially attractive as a means of pest control because it has no harmful effects on humans or other vertebrates.

An alternative approach has been to transfer the gene for this toxin directly into plants. Transgenic tobacco and tomato plants, which carried the gene, gained effective protection from insect damage. Red kidney beans are rarely eaten by insects because they carry a gene that makes a protease inhibitor. If an insect ingests the inhibitor, trypsin, one of its protein-digesting enzymes, is broken down. Introduced into tobacco plants, this gene gave better protection against a wide range of grazing insects. By making their own insecticides, transgenic plants allow biologists to direct a specific attack against insect pests. The beneficial insects such as pollinators and nectar-feeders are not generally affected.

After insects, viral and fungal parasites probably take the heaviest toll of crop plants. Resistance to a number of viral parasites has been achieved by transferring genes that make proteins of the viral coat. The presence of large amounts of these proteins acts as an inhibitor of further production, interfering with the early stages of viral replication. Through the use of 'antisense' RNA, researchers have successfully blocked the replication of several parasitic micro-organisms that attack potatoes. Success for the technique is claimed against viral, bacterial and fungal parasites.

Weeds are the major plant pests of cultivated crops. Genetic engineers have transformed wheat and maize with genes that increase their resistance to herbicides such as chlorsulfuron and glyphosphate. Proteins produced by the gene degrade or detoxify the herbicide. As a result, farmers can achieve better weed control by growing crops that are herbicide-resistant.

Late frosts in April and May frequently damage potato crops. A bacterium called *Pseudomonas syringae*, almost always present on the surface of leaves, feeds on frost-damaged plants. This bacterium helps to cause frost damage because it carries an 'ice-nucleation' gene. This gene produces a protein around which ice crystals form at temperatures between 0 and −7°C. If such bacteria are not present on a plant, ice crystals do not form until temperatures drop below −7°C.

Genetic engineers have produced so-called ice-nucleation inactive (INA−) strains of *P.syringae*, by removing the gene for ice-nucleation. Sprayed over potatoes and other crops, this strain competes favourably with those that are positive for ice-nucleation, and soon replaces them. As a result, the ice crystals do not form on treated plants unless the temperature falls below −7°C. This treatment has been used to lengthen the growing season in several frost-tender plants, including potatoes, strawberries (in which the flowers are subject to frost-damage), runner beans and dwarf beans.

8.6 MICROPROPAGATION

Micropropagation, sometimes called test-tube plant culture, is an extremely cost-effective method of producing large numbers of genetically identical, herbaceous perennials, shrubs and trees. These genetically identical plants, the product of vegetative propagation, are clones of a single parent. As an example of the advantages of micropropagation, a raspberry bush might produce from 5–20 plants from each parent in a year. Micropropagation could produce 50 000 new plants in the same time. Moreover, there would be considerable saving in terms of the space required for bedding, and in labour costs.

Micropropagation gives plant breeders a number of economic advantages. It allows them to perpetuate particular unique genotypes. Houseplants, for example, with unusual flower colours or leaf patterns, can be mass-produced from a single parent plant. In large-scale hybrid seed production, micropropagation gives breeders the large numbers of genetically uniform parent plants that they require. Plant breeders who need to store large numbers of plants, or transport them to other parts of the country, find in micropropagation a technique that saves space and cuts the cost of heating and lighting.

Four steps are generally followed in the micropropagation of plants. These are:
  (i) Selection of a suitable explant, such as a stem segment or bud, from a choice parent plant, and its **sterilisation** in sodium hypochlorite solution $(1-2\%^{W/V})$, or some other disinfectant, followed by washing in distilled water.

(ii) Transfer of the sterilised material to a **nutrient (basal) medium,** generally solidified with agar (0.7–1.0% $^{W/V}$). This medium contains salts of nitrogen, other mineral salts, sucrose, amino acids and vitamins, but generally no growth regulators. Stem explants survive for several months on this medium. Some buds elongate, forming a single short shoot with strong apical dominance; that is, preferential growth of the terminal bud, while the growth of the lateral buds is suppressed.

(iii) Transfer to a **multiplication medium,** containing indole acetic acid (IAA), to promote cell elongation, and a cytokinin such as 9–benzylaminopurine (BAP) or 6–furfurylaminopurine (kinetin), which are growth regulators that stimulate mitosis. A low cytokinin concentration stimulates the formation of a undifferentiated mass of cells called a callus (Figure 90). Higher cytokinin concentrations stimulate the formation of shoots. Both the callus and the young shoots are multiplied every 4–6 weeks by sub-culturing on the appropriate growth media. It is this sub-culturing that greatly increases the number of plantlets in the clone.

(iv) Transfer to **rooting (storage) medium.** This medium contains a relatively high concentration of IAA, indole–3–butyric acid (IBA), napthaleneacetic acid (NAA) or 2,4–dichlorophenoxyacetic acid (2,4–D), to

Figure 90   Plant micropropagation

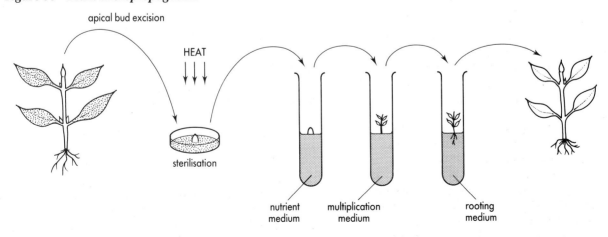

Figure 91   Stages in removing a virus from an infected plant

induce root development. After the roots have developed, the plantlets may again be subdivided, to produce many more small plantlets for further sub-culture on the same medium. As soon as these plants have reached a suitable size, they are removed and potted up in potting compost.

Micropropagation has also proved an invaluable method of removing viruses from infected plants. This possibility exists because the apical meristems or growing points of shoots are virus-free. By removing the apical bud from a virus-infected plant, and in some cases applying heat treatment, micropropagation can be used to regenerate virus-free stock. The technique has been used to good effect on potatoes, tomatoes, raspberries, strawberries and many other crop plants.

Although the advantages of micropropagation greatly outweigh the disadvantages, there are two major problems associated with the technique. The first is that micropropagation requires aseptic conditions. Failure to meet this requirement causes bacterial or fungal contamination of the culture medium, with subsequent loss of the plants that are being cultured. A second problem is an increased rate of mutation in medium-grown cells. This leads to abnormalities in the plantlets, a feature that can spread rapidly unless the technologist makes regular inspections and removes any defective individuals.

Large scale orchid production by micropropagation

A micropropagated orchid plant before transplantation from agar

QUESTIONS

1 Farmers can produce 'instant' grass' by growing seeds in trays for 8 days, under artificial illumination. Grass seedlings are watered with a solution of mineral salts, then removed and fed to cattle. A single production unit is shown in the diagram. Each of the seed trays is 50 x 50 x 10 cm.

A farmer buys a sealed metal trailer, with rear doors opening outwards, for towing behind a lorry. The trailer is 4 m high, 3 m wide and 10 m long. You are asked to convert the trailer into an 'instant grass' production unit.
a) Draw a plan and elevation of your design, to accommodate the maximum number of protection units. (Remember that you need a central gangway, wide enough for an attendant.)
b) What is the total area of 'instant grass' your unit produces every 8 days?
c) List the items you would need to set up the venture. Attempt to estimate your total costs in setting up the unit.
d) List your running costs.
e) Under what climatic condition is the unit most likely to be cost-effective?

2 Imagine you have a number of shoot cuttings from a choice potted plant. Someone asks you to micropropagate it, using each of the stages listed below:

**Select
explant**

↓

Sterilisation

↓

**Basal
nutrient
medium**

↓

**Shoot
multiplication
medium**

↓

**Shoot-tip
rooting
medium**

a) From which part of the shoot would you select the explants?
b) What solution would you use for sterilisation?
c) For how long would you leave the explants in this solution?
d) Explain the reason for a final washing in distilled water.
e) Give the names of three different nutrients in the basal medium.
f) At what point would you transfer explants from the basal to the shoot multiplication medium?
g) Give the name of a plant hormone contained in shoot multiplication medium, and its principal effect on the explants.
h) What treatment would you give to the explants after they had developed axillary branches?

i) Give the name of the plant hormone contained in shoot-tip rooting medium.
j) Outline any further treatment of the rooted cuttings.

3 What do you understand by the term 'transgenic animals'?
How may transgenic animals be produced? Discuss the current and potential uses of transgenic animals in a) agriculture and b) the production of compounds with medical (therapeutic) applications.

4 Describe, and evaluate from a scientific and economic viewpoint,
   a) the use of new breeding techniques to raise farm animals, and
   b) the use of micropropagation to mass produce plants for the home and garden.

5 Write a brief account of each of the following, emphasising their economic importance:
   a) Bovine somatotrophin (BST)
   b) Anther and pollen culture
   c) Plant protoplast production
   d) *Bacillus thuringensis*
   e) *Pseudomonas syringae*

6 The bacterium *Agrobacterium tumefaciens* causes crown gall disease in a number of dicotyledons. How have biologists exploited this bacterium in the production of transgenic plants?
As cereals are not normally attacked by this bacterium, how have biologists introduced foreign DNA into this group of plants?

BIBLIOGRAPHY

Agriculture and horticulture

Agricultural and Food Research Council (1987) *Biotechnology in Agriculture*
Hussey, G (1978) The application of tissue culture to the vegetative propagation of plants *Science Progress* (65), 258, 185-208
Lee, B (1989) Cereal transformation *Plants Today* (1), 9-11
Wilkins, CP and Dodds, JH (1983) The application of tissue culture techniques to plant genetic conservation *Science Progress* (68), 270, 259-284.

9 WATER TREATMENT AND WASTE DISPOSAL

Water treatment and waste disposal are the principal services provided by biotechnology. Humans use water for drinking, washing and flushing away excreta. As water is a natural resource, sometimes in short supply, it is important that the waste water from households should be re-cycled. This is made possible by the efficiency of modern sewage works, where organic matter, micro-organisms and chemical wastes are removed from the water before it is returned to domestic consumers. This efficiency of modern sewage plants often contrasts markedly with the conditions found on farms, where excreta from pigs and cattle may drain, via open ditches, into rivers. In the future animal excreta may be more widely processed, either to break it down into biogas, or produce a safe organic fertiliser.

Cleaning up environmental pollution caused by oil spillages, industrial effluents or agricultural chemicals is another area of waste disposal in which biotechnologists are prominent. The use of genetically-engineered bacteria to break down crude oil is one example of this type of service.

9.1 WATER PURIFICATION

Before it reaches the tap, water has usually received the following treatments:

Sedimentation → flocculation → sand filtration → chlorination

Rain water, collected in streams and rivers, is stored in reservoirs, where large particles separate out under gravity to form a sediment. Smaller particles of suspended organic matter are broken down by micro-organisms. From the reservoir water is pumped to a **mixing tank.** The addition of aluminium potassium sulphate (alum) forms a floc, consisting of fine mud particles and micro-organisms, which is removed in a flocculation tank.

The water is then filtered through a deep bed of sand. Like water that has filtered naturally through rocks, water that has passed through a **sand filter** is chemically and biologically purer than before filtration. Purification is assisted by a

mass of bacteria, algae and protozoa that builds up in the upper layers of the sand bed. Biological oxidations and reductions occur in this layer. Predatory protozoans feed on bacteria. After it has passed through a sand bed, about 99 per cent of all the bacteria and viruses in the water have been removed.

The final treatment is chlorination. Chlorine kills all the remaining bacteria, but is less effective against viruses and protozoa. The chlorine is added in sufficient amounts to provide continued protection in the water system, although there is currently some concern about these levels, based on the possibility that they might pose a long-term threat to human health.

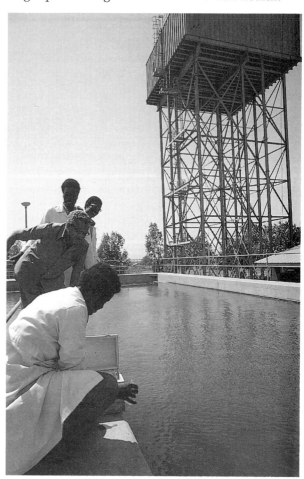

Testing the purity of drinking water in the Sudan, East Africa

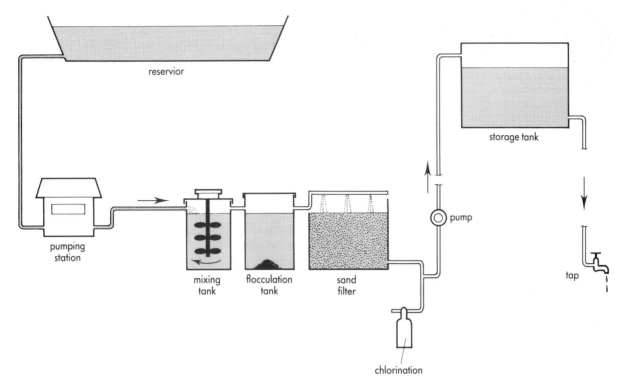

Figure 92   Stages in the treatment of the domestic water supply

Ozone, generated electrically, could provide an alternative treatment, but does not give lasting protection from pathogenic micro-organisms. Following chlorination, the disinfected water is pumped to storage tanks, situated on high ground.

9.2 SEWAGE DISPOSAL

Household sewage consists mainly of toilet wastes, bath water, handwashings and dishwashings. Sewage that enters a municipal drainage system passes to a sewage works, where it receives primary, secondary and tertiary treatments. **Primary treatment** begins at a coarse filter, where paper and other suspended or floating material is removed. In the primary settling tank, which receives raw sewage, a sewage effluent forms an upper layer above a solid sewage sludge.

   Secondary treatment of sewage effluent is carried out either in an activated sludge system or in trickling filters. The **activated sludge system** has an aeration tank, where pure oxygen or air is bubbled through the primary effluent. In this tank aerobic bacteria oxidise dissolved organic matter, and dissolved mineral salts. The principal reactions are:

$$\text{Carbon compounds} \rightarrow CO_2$$
$$NH_4^+ \rightarrow NO_3^-$$
$$H_2S \rightarrow SO_4^{2+}$$

A settling tank, next to the aeration tank,

Aerial view of a sewage treatment plant

collects a sludge formed mostly from living and dead micro-organisms. This material, or floc absorbs some soluble organic matter from the overlying effluent. Pipes beneath the sedimentation tank carry away the sludge for further processing.

   In a **trickling filter system**, primary effluent is sprayed from 4 or more rotating horizontal arms over beds of clinkers, rocks, or moulded plastic, contained in a circular concrete tank. As the effluent percolates through the beds, aerobic micro-organisms on the surface of the solid material oxidise most of the organic matter. The concrete tank retains any solid matter. Drainage pipes carry away this secondary sludge for further treatment. Bacteria belonging to *Bacillus, Proteus and Pseudomonas* species occur in aerobic treatment plants, together with an extremely important floc-forming species, *Zoogloea ramigera.* Ciliate protozoa also abound, notably *Vorticella,* whose numbers provide a useful indication of the course of microbial oxidation in activated sludge systems. The bacteria break down organic materials into smaller particles and water-soluble end products. Some of the small solid particles are digested by the ciliates.

In the final stage of secondary treatment, sewage sludge, both from the settling tank and aerobic treatment plant, is subjected to **anaerobic digestion** in a large, closed tank, normally heated to a temperature of around 30–40°C. Here, in the presence of anaerobic bacteria such as *Methanobacterium,* the volume of solids is greatly reduced, mainly by the conversion of organic compounds into gaseous end products, such as CO_2, CH_4 and H_2, along with water and mineral salts.

The tertiary treatment of sewage involves further purification of the effluent and disposal of the sludge. **Tertiary effluent treatment** removes any remaining organic matter, nitrates and phosphates. Small particles of solid material and some dissolved chemicals are removed by filtration through beds of fine sand and activated charcoal. Nitrates are converted by micro-organisms to ammonia and evaporated from stripping towers into the air. Phosphates are precipitated out by combining them with chemicals such as lime, alum or ferric chloride. Chlorine may also be added to inhibit the growth of any remaining micro-organisms, and oxidise any persistent odour-producing substances. Any water that has passed through this series of treatments is normally clean enough to be pumped into rivers. **Sewage sludge**, the solid product of sewage treatment, is of little commercial value. In many parts of the country it is emptied into the sea or incinerated. Elsewhere, after drying, it may be used for landfill or as a soil conditioner.

From time to time raw sewage, or sewage that has not completed its processing, seeps into rivers. The presence of coliform bacteria, from the human intestine, and the eggs of invertebrate gut parasites in this effluent may pose a health risk. More often, however, it poses a threat to the animal and plant life of the river. The sudden influx of a nutrient-rich solution results in increased numbers of bacteria, whose demand for oxygen is so enormous that larger organisms may become starved of oxygen. An indication of bacterial activity, and hence of the extent of sewage pollution, can be made by determining the **Biochemical Oxygen Demand (BOD)** of the water.

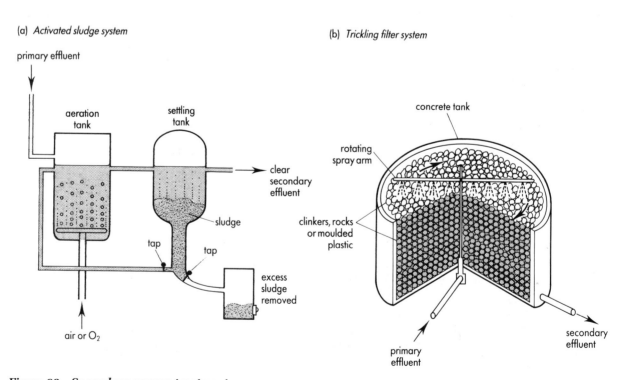

(a) *Activated sludge system*

(b) *Trickling filter system*

Figure 93   Secondary sewage treatment

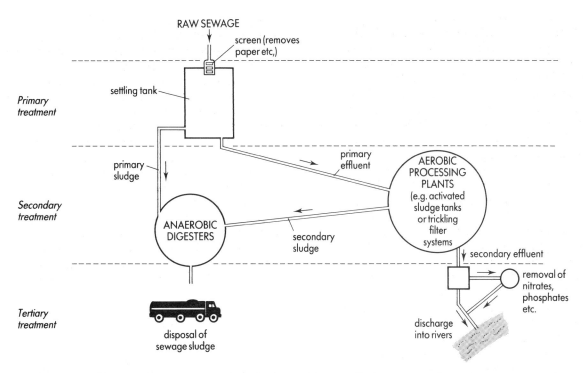

Figure 94 *General layout of a sewage works, which would normally have several aerobic processing plants and anaerobic digesters, arranged in series*

A BOD test measures the amount of oxygen absorbed by a water sample over a 5–day period at 20°C. Results bear a direct relationship to the amount of organic matter in the water. The higher the figure for oxygen consumption, the more organic matter the water sample contains.

9.2.1. Animal excreta

In isolated parts of the UK, where there is no municipal sewage disposal, farmers may use septic tanks or biogas generators to break down animal excreta. The solid matter that drains into a **septic tank** settles out under gravity, then undergoes partial decomposition to form a sludge. Liquid effluent flows from an outlet pipe in a clinker or rock-based 'soakaway', before entering the surrounding soil. Micro-organisms in the soil decompose any solid material in the effluent (Figure 95). Septic tanks require careful management and may constitute a health hazard. The sludge, for example, must be dug or pumped periodically from the holding tank. Heavy rain may cause the sewage effluent to rise, flooding the soil surface, contaminating streams, and emitting an offensive odour. There is also a risk that pathogenic coliform bacteria, present in the soil surrounding a septic tank, may contaminate farm crops.

Figure 95 *A septic tank*

Methane driven power generator

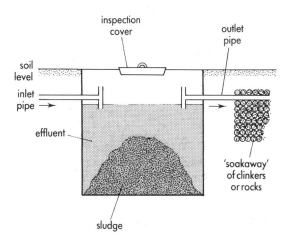

The anaerobic digestion of excreta results in the production of methane, a high-energy, clean gaseous fuel. **Biogas generators** are anaerobic digesters that produce methane from a number of organic wastes, including excreta and the leafy remains of vegetable crops. Methane production occurs in two stages:

(i)   Carbohydrates, fats and proteins are broken down by anaerobic pathways into a mixture of alcohols and fatty acids, together with CO_2 and H_2.

(ii) Methanogenic bacteria (methanogens), belonging to the genera *Methanococcus*, *Methanobacterium* and *Methanosprillum*, produce methane by reducing CO_2 with H_2:

$$CO_2 + 4H_2 \rightarrow CH_4 + 2H_2O$$

At the same time acetate, a lower fatty acid, is split to yield methane and carbon dioxide:

$$CH_3COOH \rightarrow CH_4 + CO_2$$

The gas that collects above the fermentation tank is mostly methane and carbon dioxide. It can be used as a domestic fuel, or compressed into cylinders for use in cars and tractors. Throughout China there are more than 7 million small, family scale biogas generators, making a significant contribution to the energy budget of that country. These decompose human sewage as well as the excreta from animals kept on smallholdings.

It has been known for many years that decomposing sludge soon becomes colonised by large populations of earthworms, mostly *Eisenia fetida*. The deliberate cultivation of earthworms for economic purposes is called **vermiculture**, a small and profitable branch of biotechnology. Earthworms are decomposers. They speed up the rate at which sludge and other waste materials such as straw are broken down. Any pathogenic bacteria in the sludge are destroyed as they pass through an earthworm's alimentary canal. The worm's faeces build up to form a brown-black mineral-rich organic compost, marketed through garden centres. There is also a substantial market for the worms themselves. They may be sold to improve the fertility of agricultural land, reclaim waterlogged soil, as bait for fishes or as food for a number of aquatic and terrestrial animals.

Biotechnologists have attempted to speed up the rate at which earthworms break down organic wastes. Yeasts, bacteria, energy sources (e.g. sucrose) and nitrogen sources (e.g. urea) are among additions that have been made to the raw materials. *Lumbricus rubellus*, a surface-feeding red earthworm, *Allelobophora chlorotica*, a green, shallow burrower, and *Lumbricus terrestris*, a red-brown deep burrower, have been used in combination to ensure that decomposition takes place at all levels in a heap of organic waste material.

9.3 BIODEGRADABLE POLLUTANTS

Most pollutants are biodegradable and are harmful for only a short period before they are broken down by saprophytes. Sewage for example, discharged into the sea is eventually rendered harmless by saprophytic bacteria and other organisms. Some pollutants, however, retain their harmful characteristics for a long time. **Crude oil** spilt from tankers, clings to the pebbles and rocks of beaches and devastates shore-dwelling communities, before it is eventually broken down and dispersed. The slow natural degradation of crude oil is brought about by several species of fungi, including yeasts, and bacteria belonging mainly to the genera *Pseudomonas Desulphovibrio*.

The bacterium *Pseudomonas aeruginosa* carries several different genes on its plasmids, each capable of degrading a different hydrocarbon. Distinct naphthalene-, xylene-, octane- and camphor-degrading genes have been identified. Genetic engineers have attempted to create an oil-degrading 'superbug' containing all of these genes. This task is complicated by the fact that plasmids carrying octane- and camphor-

Figure 96   A domestic biogas generator

degrading genes cannot co-exist in the same individual. By combining these two genes into a single plasmid (Figure 97), the problem has been resolved. Oil-degrading 'superbugs' are useful in dispersing small oil slicks, especially if used together with detergents, which break the oil into small droplets. Even so, the dispersal of large oil slicks still presents a major ecological problem.

Other pollutants, including lead, mercury and insecticides, persist in the environment, and accumulate in organisms through natural food chains. Bacteria that accumulate heavy metals may one day be used to remove these toxic compounds from industrial effluents. Genetically-engineered plasmids, combining genes for the degradation of various aromatic compounds, should eventually extend the range of biodegradable pollutants to insecticides, herbicides and other chlorinated hydrocarbons.

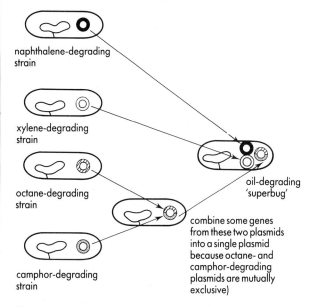

naphthalene-degrading strain

xylene-degrading strain

octane-degrading strain

camphor-degrading strain

oil-degrading 'superbug'

combine some genes from these two plasmids into a single plasmid because octane- and camphor-degrading plasmids are mutually exclusive)

Figure 97   Stages in the creation of an oil-degrading 'superbug'

QUESTIONS

1 The diagram below shows a sectional view of a water filter bed. Copy the diagram.

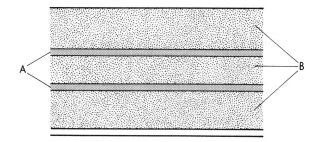

a)   Name the materials labelled A and B.
b)   State the functions of each of these materials.
c)   Label, the letter C, the layer in which most biological activity takes place.
d)   What is the chemical nature of most of this biological activity?
e)   Give the specific names of three micro-organisms that might be found in layer C.
f)   Explain the reason for periodic backflushing through layer C.
g)   After water has passed through the filter bed, what further treatment is necessary before it enters the domestic supply?
h)   Name two water pollutants that may pass through the filter bed to enter the domestic water supply.

2 The diagram below is a sectional view of a sewage treatment plant.
Copy the diagram
a)   Add the appropriate title above each tank: settling tank 1, settling tank 2, activated sludge tank, road grit separation.
b)   Explain the function of the screens.

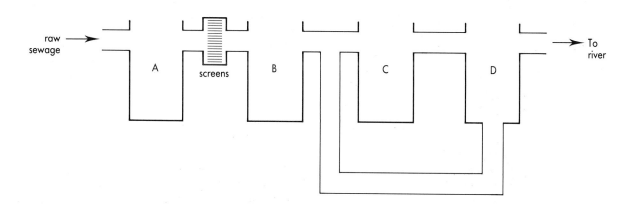

raw sewage → A   screens   B   C   D   → To river

c) In which tank are the reactions mainly
    (i) aerobic and (ii) anaerobic?
d) What is the main gaseous byproduct of the
    aerobic tank?
e) Name two additional gases that are
    byproducts from the anaerobic tank.
f) What flows (i) from tank D into the river and
    (ii) from tank D into tank C?
g) State three possible fates of sewage sludge.

3 What treatments are given to water before it
   reaches the tap? Explain the role of micro-
   organisms in water purification.

4 Describe the primary, secondary and tertiary
   processing of municipal sewage. Discuss the
   role of a) aerobic and b) anaerobic micro-
   organisms in sewage disposal. What methods
   are available for the disposal of sewage sludge?

5 Write notes on each of the following:
   a) earthworms and waste disposal
   b) septic tanks
   c) biogas generators
   d) oil-degradation by micro-organisms.

BIBLIOGRAPHY

Water treatment and waste disposal

Henderson-Sellers, B and Markland H R (1987)
    *Decaying Lakes: The Origins and control of
    Cultural Eutrophication* John Wiley and Sons
Magruder, GC and Gaddy JL (1981) Production of
    farm energy from biomass In *Advances in
    Biotechnology 2*, 269-274
Mason, CF (1981) *Biology of Freshwater
    Pollution* Longman
Salter, JH and Bull, AT (1982) Environmental
    Biotechnology: biodegradation Philosophical
    Transactions of the Royal Society, *B297,*
    575–595

GLOSSARY

Algae: aquatic, often unicellular or filamentous, photosynthetic Protoctistans, without multicellular sex organs, leaves, stems or roots

Antibiotic: an organic compound, produced by one micro-organism that kills or inhibits the growth of another micro-organism

Antibody: a protein (immunoglobulin) produced by lymphocytes in response to a foreign substance, or antigen

Anticodon: a sequence of three nucleotides in a transfer RNA molecule that is complementary to amino acid specifying codon in messenger RNA

Antigen: a foreign substance, usually a protein or polysaccharide, that stimulates antibody production

Autoradiography: a method of detecting radioactively labelled DNA (and other molecules) through expose to an X-ray sensitive photographic film

Bacteria: small, typically one-celled micro-organisms belonging to the kingdom Prokaryotae, characterised by the absence of a nucleus or membrane-bound organelles

Bacteriophage (phage): a viral parasite of bacteria, used as a cloning vector

Biomass: dry mass of organisms from any trophic (feeding) level in an ecosystem

Biosynthesis: the production of complex molecules from simple ones in any living organism

Biotechnology: the commercial exploitation of living organisms, chiefly to manufacture useful products or degrade harmful substances

Callus: an undifferentiated mass of plant tissue

Chemoautotroph: a bacterium that uses chemical energy released by specific inorganic reactions to power its life processes

Chemostat: a stirred vessel for the continuous culture of microorganisms and cells

Chimaera: an artificial hybrid, containing recombinant DNA (also used of organisms composed of cells from different species)

Clone: a population of genetically identical cells or organisms

Codon: a sequence of three nucleotides in a messenger RNA molecule that specifies one amino acid

Counter current extraction: extraction at the interface of two liquids, flowing in opposite directions

Distillation: collecting the vapours obtained from heating liquids, a method of increasing the ethanol (alcohol), content of some wines and all spirits

DNA: deoxyribonucleic acid, the genetic material of all organisms

DNA ligase: an enzyme that joins molecules of DNA together

Downstream processing: separating useful products from solvents etc. at the end of fermentation and other processes involving the use of micro-organisms

Enzyme: a protein that acts as a catalyst in reactions between organic compounds

Enzyme immobilisation: binding an enzyme immovably to a surface, so that it cannot mix with reactants or contaminate the end products

Eukaryote: a cell with membrane-bound organelles, most notably a nucleus

Fermentation: anaerobic respiration, especially the degradation to sugars to produce ethanol (alcohol)

Fermenter: the vessel (also called a bioreactor), usually made of stainless steel, used for the large-scale culture of cells or fungal hyphae

Fungus: eukaryotic organisms, without chlorophyll, that feed as saprophytes or parasites and reproduce by spores

Gel electrophoresis: the separation of molecules, according to size, in an electric field, by diffusion through a gelatinous matrix

Gene: the biological unit of a genetic information, self-reproducing and located in a definite position in a DNA molecule

Gene expression: a change in an organism resulting from the operation of a gene

Gene mapping: plotting the relative positions of genes on a DNA molecule

Gene probe: a short length of single-stranded DNA (or RNA) capable of binding to a complementary single-stranded DNA segment

Genetic engineering: changing an organism's genome by adding or deleting genes

Gene therapy: an attempt to cure genetic disorders by replacing defective genes with normal ones

Genome: all the genes present in an organism

Grana: chlorophyll-containing regions of a chloroplast, where light is trapped and ATP is made

Micropropagation: rapid, test-tube vegetative propagation of plants from small pieces of tissue called explants

Monoclonal antibodies: antibodies of a single type, typically produced by the fusion product of a cancer cell and lymphocyte

Mutagen: a chemical or physical factor capable of causing a mutation on organisms

Mycorrhiza: fungal hyphae which form a symbiotic association with plant roots

nif-genes: a cluster of genes responsible for nitrogen fixation in certain micro-organisms

Parasite: an organism that feeds on another living organism belonging to different species, causing it harm

Pathogen: a disease-causing organism

Plasmid: a double-stranded circular piece of DNA, which acts independently of the chromosome, and widely used as a cloning vector to introduce foreign DNA into bacterial and yeast cells

Prokaryote: a cell without a nucleus or other membrane-bound organelles

Promoter: a short nucleotide sequence, upstream of a gene, signalling the point at which transcription starts

Protozoa: heterotrophic, mostly unicellular, members of the phylum Protoctista

Recombinant DNA: an artificial DNA molecule, created in the laboratory by piecing together nucleotide sequences

Restriction endonucleases: enzymes used to cut DNA into shorter segments

RNA: ribonucleic acid, an intermediate in converting the genetic code of DNA into the amino acid sequence of a polypeptide

Saprophyte: an organism, notably a bacterium or fungus, that feeds on dead organic matter

Sewage sludge: the solid organic sediment that remains after raw sewage has been degraded by aerobic and anaerobic micro-organisms

Single cell protein (SCP): protein-rich, dried cellular products obtained from the large scale culture of micro-organisms

Sparger: perforated metal disc in an aerobic fermenter through which air or pure oxygen enters

Symbiosis: a physiological relationship between two organisms of different species, mutually beneficial to both participants

Synthesis: the combination of one or more molecules into one or more compounds of greater complexity

Taxonomy: the classification of organisms

Terminator: a short nucleotide sequence, downstream of a gene, signalling the point at which transcription stops

Transcription: the process in which genetic information is transferred from DNA to messenger RNA

Transgenic organism: a plant or animal into which one or more foreign genes has been artificially inserted

Translation: the process by which genetic information contained in messenger RNA is converted into a sequence of amino acids in a polypeptide

Vaccine: commercially produced antigens, usually injected in amounts sufficient to stimulate antibody production, without causing symptoms of a disease

Vector: a gene carrier, such as a bacteriophage or plasmid, used to introduce foreign DNA into cells

Virus: A minute intracellular parasite, with a nucleic acid core and protein coat

INDEX

ACKNOWLEDGEMENTS

The Publishers would like to thank the following for permission to reproduce their material:

Philip Allan Publishers (Figures 65, 76); Blackwell Scientific Publications Ltd, Plants Today, Cereal Transformation, Bruce Lee (Figure 89); Peter Gardiner (Figure 85); Institute of Biology/Association for Science Education (5); New Scientist (Figure 81).

The Publishers would like to thank the following for their permission to use their photographs in this volume:

Biophoto Associates (8, bottom left, bottom right; 11; 12; 32; 41; 59; 63; 64; 69, bottom left; 78, bottom left; 94, bottom left, bottom right); Dr Jeremy Burges/Science Photo Library (44, top); Camera Talks (19, bottom left, bottom right); CNRI/Science Photo Library (33, bottom right); David Guyan/Science Photo Library (100); Robert Isear/Science Photo Library (50); Holt Studios Ltd (33, bottom left; 44, bottom; 52; 61, top left, top right; 98, top, bottom; 101; 103); National Medical Slide Bank (30, bottom); Noro Nordisk Pharmaceuticals Ltd (46); David Parker/Science Photo Library (78, bottom right); Charlotte Raymond/Science Photo Library (69, bottom right); A Shell Photograph (85); US National Cancer Institute/Science Photo Library (30, top).

British Library Cataloguing in Publication Data
Freeland, P. W.
    Biology Focus on : micro-organisms in action.
    1. Microorganisms
    I. Title
    576

    ISBN 0 340 53268 8

First published in 1991
Second impression 1992

© 1991 Peter Freeland

All rights reserved. No part of this publication may be reproduced or transmitted in any form or by any means, electronic or mechanical, including photocopy, recording, or any information storage and retrieval system, without permission in writing from the publisher or under licence from the Copyright Licensing Agency Limited. Further details of such licences (for reprographic reproduction) may be obtained from the Copyright Licensing Agency Limited, of 90 Tottenham Court Road, London W1P 9HE.

Typeset by Litho Link Ltd, Welshpool, Powys, Wales.
Printed in Great Britain for the educational publishing division of Hodder and Stoughton Ltd, Mill Road, Dunton Green, Sevenoaks, Kent by Thomson Litho Ltd.

THE LIBRARY
GUILDFORD COLLEGE
of Further and Higher Education

Author Freeland Peter

Title Micro-organisms
in Action

Class 574 FRE

Accession 70971

WITHDRAWN